STILL ME...

To Paul.

in Memory of

Denis May Wester.

STILL ME...

BY

ALL WRITE THEN

Published by
Pewter Rose Press
www.pewter-rose-press.com

First published in Great Britain 2013
Collection © Maureen Cullen
Individual stories and poems© rests with the individual
authors
ISBN 978-1908136374

British Library Cataloguing in Publication Data
A catalogue record for this book is available from the British
Library

Cover image © Asa Fox, TheFarthestShore.com
Cover design by Emily Cooper
Printed and bound in Great Britain

All profits from the sale of each book will be donated to
Alzheimer's Society (Registered Charity Number 296645).

CONTENTS

FOREWORD

This anthology of poems and short stories is entitled, movingly enough, *Still Me...* In fact, the name is not only moving but apposite, because it seems this is the greatest struggle when dealing with Alzheimer's, that is to retain a sense that the person who is suffering is still that same dear one, that same character who has given us so much love and laughter over the years. If we were visiting a friend in prison, we would not need to be reminded that they were the same inside as they always were, but Alzheimer's is a cruel form of prison which so often consumes each inmate until there is hardly anything left of them that is recognisable.

This little book is dedicated to those sufferers of this cruel condition, certainly, but it is also a recognition of the gallantry of their carers, a reminder, I believe anyway, that these men and women are figures of honour and unselfishness and kindness, sacrificing, in many cases, their own interests and ambitions, in order to lessen the burden of the Alzheimer's victim. I salute them with all my heart.

Julian Fellowes
November 2012

This is a wonderful project – encapsulating the aims, ideals and spirit of OU Creative Writing teaching; the venture offers evidence of imagination and true writing endeavour, but also displays an admirable collaborative and interactive spirit – well done to all involved!

Derek Neale
Senior Lecturer in Creative Writing
and Chair of Advanced Creative Writing,
The Open University

INTRODUCTION

All Write Then is a group of authors who met during an Open University Creative Writing course. With our shared love of poetry and stories, we decided to compile a charity anthology to bring our new writing to a wider audience while helping a cause close to our hearts. As many in our group have family members or friends who have Alzheimer's, the Alzheimer's Society was the natural choice.

Over 800,000 people in the UK have dementia and of course, the disease directly affects many more carers, family members and friends. Our book aims to raise funds and awareness through our stories and poems, exploring the themes of love, loss and laughter. We hope we've created a collection that will touch you, make you nod along in recognition and make you laugh, and that every reader will find a favourite story or poem they want to read again and again.

Still Me... is a not-for-profit work – we have donated our time and talent. Profits will go directly to the Alzheimer's Society.

More details about the group can be found at our website www.allwritethen.wordpress.com

I'm Still Me

I struggle through wheezing gasps of raw air
which heave-haul my body first thing at dawn,
as I fight, slow my breath, defeat despair.

I creak, stiffened by sleep, my old bugbear,
cry for want of comfort, worn palm on palm,
as I struggle through wheezing gasps of raw air.

My stick crashes, pills spin, spill everywhere.
I'm a pawn of life, a woman careworn,
as I fight, slow my breath, defeat despair.

I stumble into my ramshackle chair,
grip the armrests, seeking moments of calm,
as I struggle through wheezing gasps of raw air.

I refuse to vanish, assessed for care,
finding I'm dumped without any qualms.
I fight, slow my breath to defeat despair.

Although I'm weary of this ageing affair,
a teary wait of fear, prayers and psalms,
I struggle through wheezing gasps of raw air,
slow my breath, rise, seek a choice I can bear.

Maggie Mackay

GRANNY DREAMS

When I am a granny I might be a crossover pinny
in marigold, have supersize underwear
mothballed, varicose veins,
love Domestos, and other smelly stuff.
Peering out of jelly jars
in mischief
my mouth a smooth white kerb of teeth,
my tipple, eggy-yellow Advocaat,
will I laugh a gurgle
with wrinkled leather cheeks?

Or maybe I'll be a glamour puss,
pierce my nose and belly button
– if it's still in view –
or even more tender bits of skin,
drink alcopops, dye my hair black
with fiery streaks, totter on heels,
pack my lumpy thighs
into luscious leggings, my toenails sealed
with the Union Jack,
have a rose tattoo on my bum for fun,
wear scarlet skimpies,
run a marathon …

When I am a granny I might lack
the power to pick up my feet,
put my pinny on, strut past in my thong.
I implore you, daughter and son,
dog walking will not do,
I'll be pushing ninety
when I'm pushing prams or worse,
mothballed under daisies.
So don't tarry, I'd rather be a granny
while I can be a fine disgrace,
blowing bubbles, burning cupcakes
and playing chases with my mates.

Maureen Cullen

The Elixir Of Life

As a wee nip I'd skip the birth canal
of Oaklands Drive, count twenty-five, within
which womb of rug and fug of smoking pipe
my Gramps was my divine uterine twin.
My blood, my grand leviathan of tickly tweed
and spotted cheeks and coarse sandpaper chin.
With holy hands the size of ancient shields
he stroked my hair, 'thirsty, my wee sweet thing?'

Huddled round the tap he drew the water,
holding glass to light for his grand-daughter
to gaze upon this opaque elixir
and wonder as it turned to crystal clear.

I looked up at his weathered face made blank
'Tis God's umbilicus', he boomed. I drank.

Sandy Hashimi

THE WHITE ROOM

Lynn Love

During the first days of June the staff had shaken and beaten the contents of the house, freeing every mote of dust until the air was so corrupted that passing wasps and hornets were engulfed in billowing dirt. I spent my last day of freedom in the garden, the calluses on my palms a tribute to the trees I climbed while she had been away.

Avoiding the chaos of the house, I sprawled on the lawn, a runaway in the shade of magnolias whose blushing petals had long since been swept away by the gardener's boy. My arms were limp by my sides and the clipped grass prickled my soiled skin; all was drowsy, the air close, but the warm buzz of the afternoon couldn't subdue my unease.

Mother was coming home.

I shut my eyes and realised that I could hear nothing from the house, no motor cars or gramophones, no frantic maids or gardeners and I imagined myself alone, a recluse in a world of green, dappled light, the air sugary with the scent of flowers. I listened to the whistle of air in my lungs, the dull pulse in my ears.

A banged door jolted me awake. Mother's sharp voice echoed through the house. I listened to her progress from the front door to the back as she instructed and rebuked the staff

15

in equal measure. Her shoes clicked on the parquet flooring in the hall, then fell silent as she stepped onto the deep, red rug. I scrambled to my feet as she walked through the French doors and into the garden. My hands shaking, I smoothed the wrinkles from my dress, loose blades of grass falling around me like confetti.

Mother strode across the lawn towards me, her heels snatching at the grass with each step. She paused, her face a few inches from mine. My words of greeting were throttled by fear as I watched her twitching lips. I fought to keep my face impassive under her gaze. She swayed a little, as if caught in a gust of wind; my eyes were drawn to the first hint of loose skin that sagged at her throat.

Her half-curled fist snapped my head backwards, the dull impact of her knuckles wedded to a sharp pain as her diamond ring cut my cheek. I staggered back into a border of purple alliums that filled the air with the scent of kitchens. As I stepped from the mud Mother wiped a streak of red from her trembling fingers, then calmly smoothed her hair. The society doyenne was restored but for a moment she had been a sister to the village women that she loathed, the ones who fought outside the public houses on Saturday evenings, their forearms fleshy and pink from the wash-tub, their noses swollen from drink as they staggered home with bloody knuckles and a lock of their enemy's hair as a trophy.

She had revealed her animal self and this thought calmed me as I faced a barrage of pleas and demands, of threats and refined insults. An echo of grassy dampness clung to my back as I stared up into the canopy of the magnolias. The sun was

16

now too weak to warm me and as it sank below the laurel hedge, the cold stole through my thin dress and I began to shiver.

I awoke cold and stiff. Gulls swooped past the gable, their cries echoing around the white room. The bed was stripped now, the stench of iron and carbolic finally waning. Through a window laced with ice I watched the dawn turn the sand from ashen grey to beige. The quilt dropped from my shoulder as I tilted back and forth in the chair, the fabric catching under the rocker, softening the sound of wood on floorboards. Mrs Hobbs had checked on me once or twice in the early hours; I remembered her papery hands on my forehead. She'd left a fresh jug of water on the night-stand.

Since that day under the magnolias, I had been banished from my own life. In the evening I would sit alone in the white room, with only the paint-blistered walls and a case of ragged books for company. For two hours each day I was allowed to walk the cliffs like a drab phantom, the sea holly catching my skirts as my body became alien, distended. Every moment I was watched by Mrs Hobbs or one of the women from the village. Once, I stumbled too close to the cliff edge and the white stone fell away beneath my shoe. For a still moment I hung, one foot suspended over remote, foaming waves. Then my keeper pulled me back, to fall on the cold earth where I lay weeping as if for something lost.

One night I awoke screaming, the sound of my own terror echoing within me, resonating through my hollow bones.

'Mother!'

It took me some seconds to recognise my own harsh voice and the unfamiliar sound made me cry out more urgently than before.

A web of pain spanned the tight dome of my belly, as the muscles contracted and pulsed out of my control. The door banged open and barely formed creatures emerged from the darkness, stumbling into the room. They scratched my skin with cold, rough hands and hauled my body up onto the bed. While one pulled away the quilt, others dragged my nightgown up around my waist. The hands were everywhere, pulling at my flesh, and desperate, weeping, I tore at them with jagged nails and bit the coarse skin until my arms were caught, pinned across my chest. I struggled for a few moments more, and then I fell back panting against my captor's bosom. I wept for a mother who never came, while sour breath engulfed my face.

'Is it time, d'you think?'

'O'course it's bloody time. You seen the mess.'

'Do we send for 'er ma?'

'She don't want a gatepost grandchild. Why d'you think the girl was sent here?'

'Shut up, you two.' Mrs Hobb's pale face loomed before me. 'Alright, my dove, it's early days yet, don't go wearying yourself too soon, hold a little back for the end. Daisy! Don't just stand there gawping, make yourself useful, you great lump. Go fetch some cold water to mop the girl with. Let's see 'ow we're getting on, then …'

By the early hours I lay shivering and empty on the stained

sheets, the blood surrounding my white body like a filthy halo. The women came to clean me after he had been spirited away. They held me under the armpits as I stood quivering in the tin bath, a stream of icy water flowing over a stomach soft as bread dough. They washed between my legs while I stared at the pink water lapping my ankles.

In the days afterwards I slept in the chair, swaddled in my quilt as I rocked myself to sleep. I dreamed of soft, tufted hair, the colour of my mother's fur stole, of wrinkled fists that reached out to grasp a hand that wasn't mine. Each morning my nightdress was damp with milk that should be his.

Some nights I dreamed that it was spring and I was amongst the magnolias again, the waxy blossom like goblets upturned to capture every splash of falling sunlight. As I climbed the tree my toes and fingers gripped the branches like claws, whorled bark scratching my skin. In my dreams I gazed at red pearls of blood that glistened along my limbs, while a man's coarse hands and soft words freed me from my jagged nest.

Sometimes I dreamed that I escaped the house into a cold night. Frosted grass dazzled my eyes and each step shattered the air with the crack of broken ice, crushed glass under my bare feet. An unspoken need would drive me onwards, stumbling through the dead world until I reached the cliffs. I would stand on the edge, my toes gripping the powdery stone, and stare down at the sea, itself made hard as iron by the cold, each bubble and swell perfectly captured. My foot would drift out above the void, hovering over emptiness, the lure of the numbing sea almost too much to resist. But then a pale sliver of sun would flash on the horizon and I would stumble back through a melting world, relishing the warm light of a new day on my face.

Now when the magnolias bloom I lift my son into the trees and watch as he scrambles from branch to branch, skin grazed as mine once was. I wonder if my other child, the one lost to the white room, climbs trees and picks at scabs and watches petals shower the ground. I wonder if he knows to miss me and on warm, sunny days I am almost happy with the thought that he doesn't.

In The Open

Viki Birchall

Paul felt at home in these woods; the meadow in the middle was where he had taken Amelia on their early picnics during their dating years. They had drunk warm wine amongst the knapweed, smoking and laughing in the melting sunlight. He had proposed here, the summer after they had left university. Money inherited from his grandmother had allowed him to buy a huge diamond ring and it had sparkled like her eyes in the summer sun.

The woods lay behind his childhood home, and were where he had come when his dad had got too drunk, which was frequently. This little glade hidden in the middle had resisted shrubs and was stubbornly retaining its meadowness, despite the dark surrounding woodland. Even after a private company had bought it all and turned it into an adventure park, placing footpaths and waste bins in the once secret place, he still loved to come here. So it was the place he came to the morning after the end of his relationship; the first day in eighteen and a half years without his Amelia.

No sweet wine this time, no picnic. The empty vodka bottle and pill pot lay abandoned just beyond his reach, which was perfect. He had underestimated the pain of losing Amelia and he welcomed this release.

Clouds sailed across a cobalt sky, morphing from animal shapes to trees and faces. The bright early sun pierced the tree canopy, warming his face in parts. How peaceful to lie here alone, only the whispering breeze and the distant calling of birds to interrupt his thoughts. He had hoped by this time he wouldn't be having thoughts at all, but his head was still buzzing with random memories, bouncing around his synapses like a pinball.

Paul wondered when the caw of the crows had become the excited panting of a dog. It ran past his left side, its wafting tail causing the hairs on his arms to waver like the meadow grass. He could never understand the attraction of people to dogs. They were stupid animals, loyal to even those owners who continually abused them. He hated the way Amelia had fussed over Jessie. Paul had been convinced she had loved the beast more than him.

He could hear music. He hadn't heard any footsteps, no grinding of gravel underfoot. Of course, they could have walked across the grass, despite the *Please keep to the path* signs. Still, they could have seen me here, he thought, lying beneath the tree and decided to follow suit. He really hoped not, but the music did seem to be getting louder. He could make out some familiar bars. A special song. They had listened to Billie Holiday on the cassette player in his tiny first car, listened to it over and over until the tape had become chewed and then spat out. Then he had made a new recording from the LP and listened to it some more. They had liked to park in a dark spot, up on Parson's Hill, looking down at the amber glow of the town at night. Chips, he thought. He could smell chips. They had always shared a bag of chips, the aroma clinging to the faux black leather for days afterwards, until their next romantic trip out. The muted saxophone and trumpet were meeting now, the muffled horn of her voice conveying so much emotion, as she whined about her loneliness in a way he had never before understood. It had seemed romantic back then, grown-up and ridiculously cultured. Now the words seemed so pertinent. At seventeen, when she had laughed that tinkling sound, sucking the love from his heart with her pretty eyes, he wondered if she had foreseen the passion end.

The brush caressed the snare drum as the piano played, louder and louder until the birds overhead could do little but join in. They swooped, leaving trails that he could discern. The colourful patterns made shapes, a Swiss mountain. A buzzard appeared and chased a smaller bird, possibly a swallow, their display forming the outline of the honeymoon chalet overlooking Lake Thun. How generous, he thought, that these birds were so determined to play out these scenes for him. They had left their bedroom curtains open so they could take in the sunrise, the icy water changing colour in the morning light. The peaceful ride up the grassy slopes in the chairlift had been followed by the long walk back down the mountain, the views unappreciated as they mapped out their futures: successful careers, money, a beautiful home, dinner parties with glittering crystal wine glasses and Billie Holiday playing in the background.

Raised voices. The bastards had interrupted his peace with their music. That was fine. But raised voices? Paul wanted to tell them to shut the hell up and leave him in peace. But he couldn't, so instead he lay and listened to what they had to say. The birds were still drawing their patterns for him, her face in a shade of puce left by the black crow that was probably a raven, now he looked more closely.

'Have you lost your bloody mind? Do you know what you're throwing away?'

'Yes, I know precisely what I'm getting rid of,' spat the woman. She sounded familiar, but he knew he was imagining it. 'A bully, a fat alcoholic loser who gets kicks from shouting at his employees down the phone on a Friday night. I'm sick of throwing your dinners in the bin and watching DVDs on my own, of making excuses for you when you ... when you're ...'

'Is it any wonder? You're such a stuck-up bitch. Do you think I want to come home to a bloody house full of guests after a day at work? Entertaining scroungers who only come round to drink my French wine and single malts?'

'They're your friends, you arsehole. Or were. Not any more. They hate you now, almost as much as I do. Everybody hates you, Paul.'

Harsh, he thought. Something about their argument was nagging him. Then came the thwack. Not a slap. He heard a punch. The grunt of effort told him the man was the perpetrator, the woman hadn't made a sound. He could picture her curled up on the cream carpet, blood trickling from her burst lip, her black eyes wide with shock. Paul didn't open his eyes to see if the woman was alright. It wasn't his problem anymore.

The breeze blew some grass between the fingers of his left hand, pushing them right up to the webbed parts. Like hair, he thought. Wrapped around your hand, strands becoming entangled and staying there after the head yanks itself away. She'd had so much hair that it had hardly mattered. Almost as much as that damn dog, he thought. The hair on Jessie's throat had been soft, a pale cream compared to the nicotine yellow of its back. Later, when she found her, the fur was brown. The stain on the wooden floor of the hallway refused to wash away. Amelia carpeted over it, but she had never been the same after that. Now it was her blood soaking into the hallway carpet.

The tree canopy was becoming denser, the branches closing together to block out the sun. He glanced down his body, to the photograph on his stomach that had fallen out of his hand. Her bright eyes, open-mouthed smile, her left arm wrapped around the hairy neck of a panting Labrador. Then the sun disappeared and all was dark.

THE SELKIE WIFE

Annie Shirreff

She stands at the edge of the shore as the spume of waves splashes over her bare feet. A thin cardigan is wrapped tight around her delicate frame, small defence against a sea breeze so thick with salt it parches my lips. Light from the full moon guides me towards her, the water within me pulled like the body of the sea.

It's not the first time I have found her here, staring towards the horizon. Another notch tightens on the belt around my heart. I discard my shoes and move deftly across the beach towards her, afraid her alarm at my presence might press an escape to the sea which could put us both in peril. Just as I am about to place my arms around her and gather her safely towards me, she speaks in her lilting Highland accent and I am, as ever, bewitched.

'Do you remember, Joe, when we used to come here, and how we loved to dance naked on the beach and splash in the waves? We loved the freshness of the water on our skin, and the grazing of the sand on our bodies.'

'I do.' I gently place her coat over her shoulders, slide my arms around her waist and place my chin on top of her thick crown of hair. I feel the waves stroke and suck at my toes like a lover.

'Do you think they are out there?' she asks.

'Who?'

'Those that I have left. Those that I can hardly remember.'

'I'm here,' I say, my concern rising about her mental health. She's lost weight and her black hair has faded these past months.

'You are now,' she says.

She turns in my arms. Her large eyes seem to say that maybe I can be enough. I plant a soft kiss on her lips and feel her respond. And then her body goes slack.

When I first saw Mia swim, I thought she was a seal frolicking in the waves just beyond the edge of the shore. Her thick dark hair trailed in the water as strong, smooth strokes propelled her forward. She would stop, duck her head and body under the water, and then turn back in the direction she had come.

I sat on a rock watching as the effects of the alcohol I'd consumed caused everything around me to shimmer in the midsummer light. The sky rolled with thin, pink cloud, the leaves on nearby trees gently strobed in the breeze, and waves blurred as they ran up on to the sand. She was my only clear point of focus.

She stopped for a moment and waved. I recognised her then as the girl on the dance floor at the garden party I'd just left and had marked out as someone I would like to spend time with, when the night began its inevitable wind down. But each time I'd ventured towards the spot she danced in, she'd moved to the other side of the marquee. Then she had disappeared altogether and I must have decided to come here. I could barely remember doing so.

My hair and clothes felt thick with sweat from dancing and I was tempted, in my hazed state, to cast off my clothes and join this lithe creature in the sea. I returned her gesture and walked towards the waves, my movements clumsy on the loose sand. She swam towards me, hit land and pulled herself to her feet. She was naked.

'Could you bring me my clothes over, please?' she smiled. Her soft, blue eyes held my gaze and my voice faltered.

'Where are they?'

'Over by the rocks, where you were just sat.'

I gathered her clothes and then stood watching as she tugged her shorts over the black pelt of pubic hair. Her t-shirt clung to wet curves.

'Have you seen enough?' she laughed.

'Sorry, I was just admiring – I didn't mean to be rude.'

She cupped my face in her hands and smiled before pressing her lips on mine. It wasn't long before her clothes were back on the sand.

I woke a couple of hours later under her thin suede coat. We were curled around each other and the sun was beginning to nip my face. I roused her.

'Come on, we can't lie here. I have a room back at the house.'

'I need to swim first, clean myself up. Join me?'

'I don't swim.'

She gave me a sympathetic look then plunged into the sea to wash our lovemaking from her body. I paddled about at its edge cleaning sand off as best I could. I didn't want her smell to leave me.

'Why do you not swim?' she asked as we dressed.

'I nearly drowned once.'

She nodded in understanding. I lifted her coat and led her by the hand away from the shore.

'You are not from here,' she said.

'Glasgow. I just came down for the party.'

'Are you driving back there?'

'Why, do you want a lift?'

She nodded.

'Where do you live?' I asked.

'The city now,' she said. 'There is nothing left for me here.'

Back in the city, Mia moved in to my small flat. A temporary arrangement that suited us as life settled into its daily rhythm. She worked nights in bars and made art by day. A corner of our living room was turned into a makeshift studio where she painted bold abstracts we both hoped would one day attract the attention they deserved. After a year of hard work, I got a decent promotion in my firm of architects.

'Mia,' I said, as she popped the cork on our second bottle of Moët. 'Don't you think it's time we made our arrangement more permanent?'

She frowned at my suggestion and said nothing for a few moments.

'What arrangement,' she teased. 'I live here, do I not?' She poured us both another glass of champagne and her eyes met mine as she picked up her glass and sipped.

'Let's get married,' I said. 'Buy a big house, have kids, do what everyone else does.'

'I am yours already,' she said. 'We could buy a bigger house, maybe we could even throw a party. Children though, that might be something.'

'I'm afraid it is bad news, Mrs Grey.'

I wanted to hit the walls or punch the face of the doctor who was the carrier of that bad news. But it wasn't her fault. And it wasn't ours. Our baby was gone. The little creature, which would have carried the trace of our genome into the future, had the swimming ability of its father rather than its mother. It had got stuck in the estuary which would carry it safely into the sea of Mia's womb. Mia had nearly died and they had to remove one fallopian tube. The other was fused and our chances of a natural conception were over.

'You know, there is still the possibility of IVF,' said the doctor. 'Or even adoption. I have some leaflets here.'

'I do not want IVF,' said Mia flatly. 'I have done the research and the chances of a baby are one in seven. That is too much time, effort and pain for a long shot.'

We sat quietly for a moment and then Mia addressed me. 'If it is not meant to be, then that is it. And adoption is fine for those that want it, but I do not want someone else's baby. I wanted ours.'

When we left the hospital I went straight back to my office and immersed myself in work and the setting-up of my own practice. Neither of us ever mentioned the baby word again.

We travelled the West coast on holiday, walking the hills and returning to the sea and the same beach near Tighnabruaich.

'Could we not move here?' she would ask.

'Maybe someday.'

'We could sell the house and buy a little cottage with the profit. There is work you could do here, it is not that far from the city. Or you could write, you have always wanted to. And I will paint. It would be perfect, just the two of us.' Her lip quivered. But we never did move.

Whilst I busied myself in my growing practice, Mia stayed in her studio at the top of the house and painted abstracts which told the story of her life, our life. They spoke of love. And of loss. Through small café exhibitions, she attracted a following, which led to bigger exhibitions, an agent, recognition and no small financial success.

'It is time to buy that cottage,' she said.

'But I can't move. I need to be here for work. And you know I like living in the city.'

'I am not asking you to move,' she said. 'You can come down at weekends. But I need to be by the sea.'

And so she moved. From her cottage she could look out to the sea she loved to paint and to swim in. Each weekend, when I visited, she would be caught up in her latest project. It took a little persuasion to get her to the dinner table and to spend some time with me. In the night, I often found her side of the bed empty and cold. Some of those times she was absorbed in her painting. At others, I would see her standing at the shore's edge. She looked like a fisherman's wife searching for signs of his missing vessel.

Driving along the Rest and Be Thankful, en route to

Tighnabruaich, I felt my stomach lurch and pulled over. As I looked down on Glen Croe, I imagined the ice flow gouging its way through the earth and rock, leaving the mark of its escape to the sea. It was strange to think that this timeless scene was less than an hour from the cityscape I had been helping to define. I considered the many travellers who had stood here and given thanks for reaching this point at the top of the most arduous leg of the pass.

Is this what we had reached, Mia and I? What had happened to us? Each time I visited her, she seemed further away than before. It was not just her obsession with her art and the sea. There was something else. Something I couldn't change or make better. I hadn't visited for two weeks and apart from a few texts we hadn't communicated. I missed her.

I arrived and called for her, checking the small bedrooms, kitchen and living room. The walls of this large, but tastefully shabby room were covered in her paintings. I traced the story of our life together through the colours: red splashes on raw canvas, thick black lines, and the large blue abstracts of seascapes, which had become something of an obsession. Every surface held small sculptures, fashioned from the shells and driftwood she had a habit of collecting on her rambling walks along the shore.

There was no sign of her. Outside, her collection of shells and pebbles spilled from the house and formed pathways between well-tended shrubs, purple rhododendrons and red roses. The air was heady with their essence as they jostled for attention through the green backdrop.

But Mia was not there.

There was only one place left. Even at midsummer, it was cold down there at night. I walked through the house to the front, opened the boot of my car and retrieved Mia's suede coat, the same one we had slept under that first night together. Then I went to find her.

As I walked down the shore path, I saw her.

Mia collapses in my arms. There is no substance to her. I lift her easily from the shore, bring her indoors and lay her on the couch in the living room. She appears to be sleeping. I am just about to phone for help when she speaks.

'Do you remember that first time we met?'

'Of course, how could I forget? I thought you were a seal in the water. I'd never seen anyone swim quite like you.'

'No. It was just before that,' she says.

I'm puzzled. But then, as if yanked by a rein, my mind leaps back to that time. And I do remember. 'You?'

'You had swum too far out to make it back on your own, had turned deathly pale. You would have made a fine statue for a selkie's garden. But when I looked at you, at your face, I fell.' Mia waits as I absorb. 'You had swallowed more water than was safe, could not keep your head up long enough to breathe. And I could not do it. I carried you on my back to the shore, pushed you up onto the sand where you were safe and waited until the sea pulled away.'

'I have wondered about that night. I was drunk, confused. I thought it was maybe a dream.'

She shakes her head. 'I waited until you woke. I watched from the sea as you dressed and settled yourself on the rock. I had left my skin. But you have always known. You may have hidden it from yourself. But you knew.' She pauses. 'Why Joe?'

I think about the past year, my refusal to move, to be with her as she's needed. But I can't answer.

'I was never enough for you,' she says.

'And now?' I ask.

'And now? Now, I need to go back.'

I want to argue with her, to tell her that she's wrong, that I can change, that we belong together. But instead, I lie on the couch with her and hold her tight until we both fall asleep. When I wake, she's gone.

As I walk to the shore, my heart is a stone in my chest. With each breath it feels like a shard of the stone breaks free and rattles against my ribs. I stand at the edge of the shoreline, watching as the waves rise over the beach and mix with the sand in their wake. But when the waves recede, the sand always remains.

Gone Fishing

Elizabeth Angus

Through the cool morning went the woman, towards the loch. She walked the rough track between the drystane dykes, the road a little dusty, the stones of the walls sucking dim warmth from the autumn sun. On the verge, the dog rustled through the rust-orange leaves, nose down, tail up. The damp spicy scent of brambles hung heavy in the air. Day upon day for six days it had been the same. Pearly strings of spider web drooped from the thorns. From a bush, a blackbird scolded.

The woman left the road and followed the path that cut down to the water. The way was edged by ancient stunted oaks, which held out their arms above her, blocking the sky. Mangrove-like, they cooled their twisted old toes in the shallows. Down here there was no sun. A thick fog lay on the water, bright white. The water was bright white too, mirroring no reflection. The air was wet and intensely cold, and great breaths of mist crawled in across the loch. The woman's own breath hung round her.

The dog trotted up and down the shoreline. It flushed a rabbit but paid it no heed, intent on its own course. The woman sat on a rock and waited. For the past six days it had been the same. Looking over the loch there was nothing to see, white fog seamlessly merging with white water. High overhead, through a gap in the haze, three gulls flew across a patch of blue. Sunlight ricocheted white off their bright undersides. She wanted to fly with them.

But down here all was still cold and white. From out of the mist came sounds and no sounds: traffic far across the water; cows in the sunlight fields behind her; swans very close, but out of sight. Everything sounded dull and sharp and somewhere else, not here. Here was hush and chill and waiting. A buzzard wailed in the air above.

The dog did not sit with her but ceaselessly paced up and down the shore. Sometimes it would come close and look at her – why are we waiting? Why don't we go? – then pad away again, compelled to keep moving by some force neither she nor it understood, its uneasy tail down.

Then, ten yards away, the fish jumped. Every day he had burst from the bright water, at first far from shore but drawing closer as the days passed. Now, on the seventh day, luminous silver-grey, he looked at her. He smiled.

Come on in.

The water's lovely.

The dog automatically padded up and down the shore for a while longer. Then it trotted back to the dusty warm road where the blackbird sang and made for home, tail down, alone. Neither she nor it ever returned to the shore.

DEATH OF A PLASHACK

Did the bridges break thee,
humble sons of Galilee, gathered
on that bleak tip of Black Isle
where hippies and outlaws, never
brought up to it, clambered
like children over rocks at Rosemarkie
and spent their days trokin highs.

What changed on this land that bears
a strange light, did they bring
new fish to your plate, no biggar-man,
thee, who with never a curse carried out
droog-droogle in thine bauchles –
mair even than the Jenny mucks –
whilst watching tumblers in the ocean.

At now kucka, no-one knows how
to barb a hook. Were you there
before Him, or was the Lord aboot thee
the day the last of the plashack died.

Sharon MacGregor

Written in memory of Bobby Hogg, the last speaker of the Cromarty fisherfolk dialect, who died in October 2012.

In interviews, he said it was believed the fisherfolk were descended from those at Galilee. They were very religious, never swore, and used the Lord's name in their speech, though never in a blasphemous way. They had their own names for fish.

Glossary

plashack: plaice
trokin: dealing/bartering
biggar-man: large flounder
droog-droogle: heavy work in wet weather
bauchles: old, worn shoes
mair: more
Jenny mucks: women working the land
tumblers: porpoise or dolphins
At now kucka:(a greeting) – what are you up to, friend
no-one knows how to barb a hook: no-one knows how to speak the dialect of the fishermen

39

When I Was Very Young

My Grandma's pelargoniums, crowned
with purple airy umbrels,
frothing, foaming, over-
spilling, stand in saucers on the ground:
moss-grown Minton, shabby Spode.

Stooped, hand on hoe,
Granddad walks the tightrope planks
between the rows.
First earlies, second earlies, maincrop.
Arran Pilot, Beauty of Bute,
Sharpe's Express and Pentland Dell –
he's earthing-up
        and banishing to Beastie Hell
leatherjackets, eariewigs, wireworms:
slain with a sliver of slate.

Plum-tree'd walls wrapped round the sun,
the cabbage whites and carrots;
round bumble bees in clover,
pretty traps the secret spider spun,
fragile daisy chains; and me.

Elizabeth Angus

Paisley Summertime, 1955

My baby face shines like polished ice
The '55 heat wave burns potent and fast.
Pots, pans, a kettle battle; I play in paradise,
in my childhood back garden, many years past.

The '55 heat wave burns potent and fast.
Gran's eyes watch from a scullery distance.
In my childhood back garden, many years past,
I'm her favourite summer fruit fragrance.

Gran's eyes watch from a scullery distance,
as Auntie and I wait for the Brownie to click.
I'm her favourite summer fruit fragrance,
clutching Teddy from my toy box pick and mix.

'Margaret'. Auntie and I both look up; the Brownie clicks,
My Clarke shoes scrape, their giant bows flop and flap,
I'm clutching Teddy from my toy box pick and mix.
An oversized trike judders as my toes gently tap.

My Clarke shoes scrape; their giant bows flop and flap.
Pots, pans, a kettle battle; I play in paradise.
An oversized trike judders as my toes gently tap.
My baby face shines like polished ice.

Maggie Mackay

THE MAGIC GARDEN

Lynn Love

Sometimes I tell people that when I was a child our soot-stained terraced house had a Magic Garden. They'll look for the sparkle in my eye and they'll laugh and say, 'how funny.' But when my eyes fail to glitter and I don't laugh along they look uncomfortable until eventually they cave under the weight of their own curiosity and ask 'how?' or 'why?' and I tell them.

I tell them about the forest where a growling bear lived and a crane stood sentry to guard me from danger. And, if you sat in the dark and were quiet and still, the statues would come to life and weed and sweep to save my father's aching back. I tell them of the black castle guarded by a metal dragon with snapping jaws and claws like daggers.

And I tell them about the day the magic stopped.

Up to the age of seven I lived my life outdoors, not on the city streets, among the children who threw stones at gaunt stray dogs. I preferred to spend my time in our yard, our 'garden' as Mum would call it.

The garden was long, with a paved strip down the middle and wide flowerbeds on either side that stretched from the back door to the gate. This gate was tall, wooden, with blistered, curled paint. It looked like a giant bird moulting feathers. It wore at least five colours of paint, three of them different shades of blue.

In autumn I would jump in piles of leaves that had fallen from the sycamore that stretched its limbs over our back wall, and in winter I would stand on frosty puddles, aching to hear the crack of ice and watch the splinters spread beneath my feet.

Spring and summer were the best of all. Then the flowerbed that bordered our neighbour's garden was filled with wigwams of runner beans, their scarlet blooms nodding with the weight of furry bees. Opposite the beans, along the fence that defended our garden from the wilderness of the alleyway, were tomatoes with yellow flowers that one of my friends said were captured stars. The toms would grow to just above my head but the runners would grow forever until the tendrils ran out of pole and drooped back towards the earth. It was there, among the forests of heart-shaped bean leaves that I would sit when the sun was baking the yard, turning the moss from bright green, and the hair-thin spikes to fields of microscopic straw.

My friends and I would sit together in the forest and drink our tea from the caps of Teacher's whisky bottles, eat bread and butter from jam-jar lid plates and swap fairy tales about the Magic Garden and the creatures that lived there.

First of my friends was Looby-Loo, a rag doll with a floppy neck who told sad stories about girls sent to sleep by a prick of a needle or a sip of magic potion. I liked Looby but her stories always ended with the maidens being left to sleep until their hair turned grey and their faces were puckered like dry shammy leather. We didn't ask Looby-Loo to tell us stories very often.

Then there was a teddy bear called Gordon who was my best friend even though his paws and the end of his nose were bald and he smelt like sour milk. He had a growl in his stomach and when you turned him upside down he made a noise like he was hungry. Gordon was fearless and told stories about a hero who sliced off a monster's head with a talking blade, snicker-snack! It was Gordon who first told me about Dad.

Next there was Delilah, a china doll who had a missing hand that no-one ever talked about. I heard the name at Sunday school once and loved the feel of it on my tongue: De – li – lah. Delilah's cheeks were white where the paint had rubbed off and she told mean stories where the wicked witch baked brave children in an oven or enslaved them in a mine, forcing them to pull coal trucks like pit ponies until they'd learned to talk politely to adults. I preferred Gordon's stories.

Swelling the audience were a family of peg dolls I had made one Christmas when the adults were laughing too loudly and splashing beer on the antimacassars. The dolls were clothed in odds of Christmas wrapping paper and ends of ribbon, and wore finger-knitted scarves; I had mastered the skill just the week before. They didn't have names of their own but were called 'The Bobbins' like they were an acrobatic group at the London Palladium. Sometimes I would push their peg legs into the garden soil and they would listen to the stories, silent and solemn until it was time for them to sleep in the gold and green of their tobacco tin bed.

The shed was the only part of the garden that wasn't mine. The house was Mum's. It was forever filled with the scent of meat puddings and there were doilies that covered every polished surface. The ornaments in the garden were Mum's too: the crane that stood on one leg and the stone frog with his chipped green paint that hid under courgette leaves that rustled like dry umbrellas. There were also gnomes in red caps with fishing rods and wheelbarrows. I knew the gnomes helped Dad to tend the garden because there were always leaves in the wheelbarrow, as if they hadn't had time to empty it before the sun came up and they were frozen still again. Two concrete hens stood by a rambling patch of web-spun ivy and one Easter morning, tucked by their claws, I found a nest and five chocolate eggs, each wrapped in shimmering foil.

I let Dad plant his vegetables, although it always felt like my garden. But the shed was his alone. The wood was brown, so dark it sucked light from the air, surrounding itself in shadow, or so it seemed to me. Sometimes it dripped black liquid that smelt like car engines. Gordon said perhaps it was the shed crying but Looby-Loo argued that only children cry, or princesses when they're locked in tall towers. The shed door had a heavy padlock and the key was kept out of my reach on a hook in the kitchen. Even so, my parents told me to leave the shed alone, it was a dangerous place filled with things that could hurt me.

When Dad went into the shed I would perch on the end of a railway sleeper, my back resting against the crane's legs. He was my lookout: alert and always watchful. I would stretch my ears, trying to catch every bang or scratch or clang of metal.

All the while my dad was inside he would swear, cursing like he did when he listened to football on the radio. Soon the noise would stop and Dad would emerge triumphant with a bucket or a screwdriver.

At first the noises confused and frightened me. Then one afternoon when the air was heavy with moisture and thick with the buzz and hum of insects, Gordon told me the story of Castle Shed. In his rumbling voice he told of a fortress stuffed with treasures guarded by a fearsome creature with eyes like smouldering coals and a tongue of leather that would snap from its jaws like a whip to catch its enemy a stinging blow. The dragon had claws like the contents of a cutlery drawer, each one honed to pinprick sharpness. The creature's wings could span our best room, but if it did it would drip the same foul liquid that seeped from the shed all over Mum's doilies, until the rug was soaked and slipped under your feet.

Gordon told me it was my dad who had captured the creature and chained it inside the castle, so it couldn't scythe down the runner beans with its cutlery claws and singe Mum's nets with its ember eyes.

It all made sense to me. That was why the shed had to be padlocked, why it was so dangerous for me to go inside. Dad swore while he was in there because he was subduing the monster. That was why some days it sounded like the shed was collapsing from the inside.

I'd always adored my dad. He was funny and made a good pony on rainy Sunday afternoons. But now he seemed like St. George, only sporting a jumper instead of armour, and he was a hero because he fought a monster to keep me and Mum safe.

When Dad ducked inside Castle Shed I would translate the noises, here the scrape of metal claws, there the rasp of rusted teeth. It sounded as though each time Dad went inside the shed the dragon was fiercer, sharpening its talons and gnashing its jaws, chafing at captivity. I would listen, my stomach hollow and sickened like I had a tummy bug, certain the dragon was preparing itself, but for what I didn't know.

From then on every dream was filled with a whir of iron-brown blades and Dad's terrified eyes. I was always there, my voice stolen, caught in the dragon's spell as its wings opened with a leathery crack. One morning I woke shivering, my pillow damp where I'd been crying. With my heart fluttering like a Cabbage White's wings I knew I had to help my dad to be free of the dragon for good.

Gordon helped me to hatch a plan and, after several days perched by the crane's beanpole legs, the moment came. Dad clumped past the railway sleeper in his work boots. Mum had to be out – there was no way he would walk through the house like that if she was home. I was relieved she was gone. I didn't want her to be frightened too.

Nerves fizzed through me like bubbles in cream soda. I took a deep breath. I could hear the ragged pulse in my ears. Dad undid the padlock and hung it from the hasp. I reached for my sword, a bamboo cane with a split end Gordon and I had chosen for its weight and its sharpness. I held it in my damp palm, hoping it wouldn't slip when it came to the kill. I tried not to think of the dragon's fangs, of its dripping jaws. I lifted my shield, a tin Four Boys advert Dad had found on a skip. Panting with the effort, my arm trembling, I shuffled

47

towards danger.

Dad pulled on the door. I held my breath. The wood snagged on the frame and he had to pull again. I had a vision of the dragon, one claw dug into the black planks. I could barely breathe, the smell was so strong it made me gag. Dad tugged the door and it swung open. I raised my sword, ready to strike …

'Good God, love! What the bloody hell are you doing?'

I had jabbed him in the calf with my sword.

'You made me jump,' he said, rubbing his leg. He eyed the Four Boys. 'What're you doing?'

I swallowed hard, watching the rank darkness for movement. 'Dragon,' I whispered.

He followed my gaze. 'Bless you, there's no dragon in there. C'mon and I'll show you.' He took the shield from my sweaty fist, turned towards the shed and stopped. 'Just put the bloody stick down, will you? I don't need poking in the arse.'

Breathless, I did as I was told and followed him cautiously inside, watching the shadows. I was being initiated into a male domain and it made me feel itchy. The shelves were strung with spiders' webs and the hollow shells of snails no bigger than my little finger nail. Everywhere there was a chaos of rusting metal: the jagged teeth of a saw, the jaws of a vice, all dismembered and stacked in boxes. Dad stroked the tools sadly.

'Your granddad's these, though he'd leather me if he saw them in this state.'

On the floor was a tin bucket containing a dark liquid. As I drew closer the smell became stronger and I knew what it was:

dragon's blood. Perhaps Dad had saved it because of its magical powers. Maybe it could cure a festering dragon bite or give strength to warriors heading into battle. Wishing I was still armed, I edged forward and nudged the bucket with the toe of my sandal. The glossy surface rippled lazily. I watched as smaller ripples, like echoes, travelled across the dragon blood, becoming fainter until it was a black mirror again, a nightmarish vision of Dad's shed captured inside it. Strange, I thought, it smelled like the main road in June when workmen had encased the cobbles with steaming gravel.

'That's creosote,' he said, seeing me staring. 'I paint the shed with it to stop it rotting.'

After half an hour during which Dad picked through a jumble of rust-coloured bones, he finally found the hammer he needed and we locked the door behind us. By then Mum was home and it was meat and potato pie for tea. It was only as I lay in bed that night that I realised Gordon was still outside, prey to silvery slug trails and pearls of dew.

HOME

Jackie Burgoyne

Ron wakes to the sound of a particularly noisy seagull squabble. Pale grey light shines through a gap in the curtains and the air has a chill in it. Stretching, he feels a surge of energy and moves across to the edge of his low bed. He is aware of a feeling of purpose, though he can't quite pin it down. It is 5.30 a.m, the time he rose every day for forty-five years when he worked in the depot.

A deep red jumper is folded neatly on a chair. Sliding it over his head, he feels the soft warmth of the wool on his cheeks, then under his palms as he smoothes down the sleeves. His old cap peeps from the top of the wardrobe. He pokes it with his walking stick, laughing when he manages to knock it down. He plops it on his head and pulls it into just the right position, the peak in the middle of his forehead.

Ron is used to being quiet when he wakes, from years of not disturbing his wife and children. But now he doesn't need to creep down the stairs, his bedroom is on the ground floor, in what used to be the dining room. As he walks into the hall, he sees the sun shining through the glass of the front door. He fiddles with the key for a few minutes until his hands remember the right actions and the door is unlocked and open. Closing it quietly behind him, he leans lightly on his stick and makes his way to the end of the road.

Wendy's head slumps heavily on her pillow. Her neck is stiff and her belly sore, from the long pull of anxiety on her muscles. Her alarm clock says 8.00 a.m. Dad must have slept in, tired from his trip to the doctor's yesterday. Wendy slides to the edge of the bed and puts on a pink dressing gown with the satin shape of an elephant on the pocket, a present from her brother, Simon. Well, chosen by Helen more likely and not too diplomatic a gift. She moves slowly to the bathroom. When did she stiffen up like this?

If she leaves Dad sleeping, perhaps she's got time for a shower. She'd risked popping out to the Co-op yesterday. Just to get some milk. Dad was sat in his armchair, listening to his Welsh choral music. Smiling, dozing. It was fine. But she'd glanced at her reflection in the shop window and realised she hadn't brushed her hair. Unwashed clumps were sticking up all over the place.

Wendy steps into the walk-in shower and takes advantage of the plastic seat installed for Dad. Warm water gushes over her hair and face and she sits, breathing deeply for a few moments. Working her herbal shampoo into her scalp, she feels the greasiness melt away. She soaps her heavy body and rinses, rinses until her limbs are pink. Realising she hasn't listened out for Dad for a few minutes, she turns off the shower and wraps herself in a towel. All quiet.

Wendy thinks of getting dressed before she checks on Dad. She knows going into his room will wake him and then he'll need her full attention. But it's nearly nine now and it's unusual for him to sleep this late. Instead, she puts her dressing gown back on over her damp skin and makes her way down the stairs. She opens the door of Dad's bedroom quietly, wanting to wake him gently, to reassure him in those first few waking minutes when he's especially confused. Looking across for the sight of her sleeping father, she sees only an empty bed.

Ron spots the pub on the corner, *The Lamb*. Here, every year in July, they offer a tot of rum to ex-navy men like himself. They're all getting on a bit now of course and he smiles at the thought of the tottering and drunken laughter that follows. He's forgotten he hasn't been able to go for a few years; with the concoction of medication he's taking even a tipple would have him half-collapsed.

He walks on down towards the square, a collection of mismatched shops and houses forming the centre of this small island community. He's passing through just before it begins to wake for the day. In the next hour the newsagents will open, the dustbin lorry will begin its noisy clatter, the paper boys and girls will stream from the shop to the surrounding streets. But for now only a fox, big and healthy, dashes across the road into the park.

Ron catches a sound, listens for it, then realises it's coming from his own lips. He is whistling, puffing out a tuneless version of *The Night has a Thousand Eyes*. He has the chorus, but is trying to work out how the verse goes. His absorption in this is complete and he doesn't look where he's going. Instead, his legs follow a familiar pattern, taking him through the square, past the Co-op, the electrical store, the charity shop.

There is a picture in the window, Christ on the cross, a woman lying distraught at his feet. Ron has never been much of a one for religion and the image doesn't draw him closer.

Wendy tries to swallow, but the lump in her throat prevents it. Calling for Dad, she searches the cloakroom, the living room, the kitchen. She looks upstairs, in the bathroom, her bedroom, the spare room piled with belongings. She runs back down the stairs, checks all the rooms again, and then takes the back door into the garden. For a moment, she feels hopeful. Dad sometimes sits out here, even pulls up those weeds his hand and eye recognise from long ago. But the hope is short lived, the door is locked and if he had gone out there, he couldn't have locked it behind him. She looks in the garden anyway, but the bench is empty and the plot isn't big enough for him to be hidden anywhere. A sob rises in her throat and she realises tears must have been streaming down her face for some time. She freezes, her arms wrapped around her body, clinging to herself, holding herself upright.

'Come on Wendy,' she tells herself. 'Panicking isn't going to help.' She goes back in the house and reluctantly tries the front door. It is unlocked. How could she possibly have forgotten to lock it last night? She always leaves the key in the lock, so they could get out quickly in case of fire. She had worried about doing this, but lying sleepless one night, she had imagined trying to lead Dad through a smoke filled house, trying to find the key to unlock the door.

Looking up and down the road, she sees only the paperboy.

'Tom! You haven't seen my dad have you?'

53

He shakes his head. Should she dash down the road, to see if she can spot him in the square? But she knows she'd be slow and is wearing her dressing gown and slippers. The police. She must ring them. The conversation is tortuous. The clerk who responds to her 999 call insists on taking all her details first. As she gives her name, address, age and phone number, she can see the hands on the wall clock marking the passing minutes. A missing person. Is it a child? No. Has he been missing for 24 hours? No, but …

From somewhere, she drags up language from a carers' training course, taken long ago. 'He's a vulnerable adult.' That seems to give the right signals, fit with whatever's written on their checklist. They realise it's urgent. They'll send someone over. She's told she must try and find a recent photograph. But first, Wendy thinks, she must phone her brother and sister.

Ron makes his way up the long, steep hill to the top of the island. There are few houses in this part, a Community Hall, the recycling depot. When he reaches the top, he sits for a moment outside a disused petrol garage. His sense of purpose remains, but he is relying on intuition to fulfil it. At the side of the pavement opposite is a landmark he recognises, an old milestone. He wanders across the road, sweeps his hand across its smooth stone and fingers its rough lettering. His legs take him across a piece of scrubland to the steep cliff path, which descends to the bottom of the island. He looks over the edge and stands there, staring at the coast sprawling out below him. But he feels the biting cold blowing deep into his legs and turns back. Instead, he makes his way back to the road and follows the curving pavement of this gentler decline.

Wendy fumbles with the phone, dropping it as she tries to take it from its recharger. Laura isn't answering. Taking the kids to school, probably. Each ring seems to stretch into minutes. She tries Simon. Thank goodness, he answers.

'I'm on my way into work Wendy, can you ring me back later?'

'No, Simon, Simon, it's Dad.'

'Oh God Wendy, you're not panicking again are you?'

'Yes … no, he's missing, Simon.'

'Missing, what on earth do you mean?'

'Missing, gone, not at bloody home, I don't know where he is. What do you think I mean?'

'For Christ's sake, I thought you were meant to be looking after him. I said he'd be better off in a care home. Have you called the police?'

'Yes, they're on their way.'

'Well there's more point talking to them than me. There's not much I can do from up here. Ring me when you know something.'

'Simon, can you ring Laura?'

But he had gone.

Ron walks down the hill, way-marked by more pubs, *The Victoria, The King's Arms, The Dolphin*, all familiar to him from years gone by. He pictures his hand raised, holding a dart, poised, delicate. Throwing it, at just the right angle, with just the right pressure, to hit the bullseye. A bull finish. He hears the roar of his team-mates around him, feels the slaps on his back, tastes the frothy edge of the celebratory beers.

Turning the corner, he sees the chip shop, now a Chinese restaurant and feels his first pang of hunger. He continues down a lane, the position and shape of which is familiar, but the houses he remembers as wrecks are refurbished as holiday homes. Crossing the car park at the bottom, he makes his way to the destination he has held not in his head, but his heart.

Wendy is sitting in her living room, clutching a photograph of her dad, taken at Laura's wedding, ten years ago. Someone, she's not sure who, has made her a cup of tea. She has described the red jumper she knows Dad is wearing, a present from Simon, left unworn on the chair because of the label: *Wool and mohair. Gentle hand-wash only. Dry flat.* The policeman is talking in a low monotone.

'Research suggests missing vulnerable adults are most frequently found in the vicinity of their home.' Research? What the hell was he talking about?

'We have a squad car driving round the top of the island and two officers making house to house enquiries.'

Wendy gathers her wits to try and explain.

'You know most of the island isn't accessible by road? He could wander for miles round the old quarries and no one would see him.'

'I know it's hard for you Mrs ... er ...'

'Miss. Stanforth. The same as my dad. You did get his name, didn't you? What about the helicopter? Shall I call the coastguard?'

'Yes of course. Stanforth. We have our tried and tested procedures Mrs Stanforth. Let's see what the officers can find out before we go down the route of contacting our coastguard colleagues.'

'There you are my lovely,' Ron says. 'There you are my beauty.'

The beach. The waves roar a welcome to him. The pebbles fall and crunch under his feet. More agile people stumble on this shingle bank, but Ron's feet know just how to move to accommodate the drifting of the pebbles beneath them. He makes his way to the sea. The wind is now a gale, but is South-Easterly, so supports him in his place on the water's edge. The spray washes into his face. Images form, whether these are in front of his eyes or behind them, he cannot be sure. A sunny day, children, two girls and a boy, playing, squabbling. A dark haired woman, beautiful, unpacking sandwiches from greaseproof paper. A small fishing tent, a paraffin fire that keeps going out. He feels the tug of a fishing rod as he hauls out mackerel after mackerel, as big and handsome as tabby cats. The sea air is as familiar to him as his own skin. He is suffused with a feeling he cannot name, but he mouths his closest approximation.

'Home,' he says. 'Home.'

A little further around the bay, a dog walker looks across and sees a windswept old man, wearing a jumper over pyjama trousers and slippers. She feels in her pocket for her mobile phone.

The Stirrer

she was locked in the kitchen
your grandma
a self-imposed exile
stuck to the stove
stirring

on sleepy school mornings
she stood
bent back to the door
prodding the porridge with
long blackened spurtle
all worn away at the tip

dinner at noon, and the room
was warm with the smell of her soup
on flour-dust afternoons
she beat up the batter
the strength of the woman all there
in her fat-spattered arms

though the sun gave up
and went down
still she'd be stirring;
a cailleach's cauldron of custard
clung yellow against the dark wood

and then
when you'd gone to bed
she'd finally sit
swirling a sherry, watching the soot
burn at the back of the fire

nodding her head

Elizabeth Angus

cailleach (gaelic) – old woman; hag; goddess of winter

TREASURE

I remember when the meter man came jingling
into our kitchen. Soon the tin box sat square
on the scratched melamine. It gawped
like it had been woken from its dreams.

Something was up. Someone had plopped
a penny in the pond of my mother's face.
It rippled and smoothed as columns of coins
grew. Treasure. I had never seen so many in one go.

The box always swallowed her shillings tight-lipped,
now silver tubes slid towards her. She smiled.
I stared in wonder: a windfall, a rebate.
We giggled as the meter man jingled out.

Maureen Cullen

First Published In Writers' Forum Issue 131

JEELY JARS

I could have done with the yellow scales today.
Who got them, and the Kenwood?
Not Mum (Cook-In sauces, béchamel packets).
Not her.

Who got the tablespoons with the long
handles, the cake tins stacked together
ready to be greased with Stork SB?
Who got the melty plastic jug?

I got the photos.
Glamorous Granny on a cruise
Pat, white-haired, white dinner-jacketed
bookending a waiter with a tower of glasses
laughing like he was magic.

Pictures are no good today. Today
(flush-faced, peering into a rolling boil)
I want to put my fingers where yours were.
Tap-dance on your lino
bake without a recipe
lick the ancient wooden spoon
kiss you goodbye as I run away
heavy with cake and secret scrunched-up fivers.

Jo Laidlaw

THE VANISHING MAN

Lynn Love

I had lost my father once before.

When I was a child he seemed monumental, tall enough to eclipse the sun when he collected me from the playground. When I snuggled into the warm cave of his shoulder he was refuge and bear combined; rocky and growling, his paws sheltered me from sticks and stones and mercurial friendships, the battlegrounds of school. I never questioned his solidity.

His first disappearance was gradual and began when I was thirteen. It was a Sunday afternoon, the fug of pork and cabbage still lingered over the worn Axminster and *The Great Escape* was on the television. I had waited all weekend for a natural disaster; the house being swallowed by the old mines that ran underneath it would've done or perhaps a tidal wave would tear up the Bristol Channel and rip the city from its foundations. But nothing came to save me from my maths homework.

I had postponed the inevitable as long as I dared by watching Richard Attenborough discuss soil removal and tunnel ventilation. I glanced around the front room, searching further distraction when I looked towards Dad. He was slumped in his usual chair, the seat sagging, his companion – the overflowing ashtray – teetering on the arm. Through a quiff slick with Brylcreem, I glimpsed the brown and purple swirls of the lounge wallpaper. Through his chest I could see the rambling tea roses that decorated the chair back. I thought nothing of it. I just dragged myself away to do battle with those twin monsters, Algebra and Logarithms.

From then on I would snatch glimpses of him: a shadow loitering at the back of awkward family photographs, a grumbling voice over the breakfast table, a barked order hardly audible from the battlement that was my bedroom door.

At eighteen I left home and my father winked out of existence. He would reappear once a year over mountains of sprouts and the stodgy horrors of Christmas pudding and the Queen's speech. He materialised during the summer if Mum could persuade me to come home, where I'd be recaptured in childhood by the single divan, caged by the Pierrot duvet cover I loved when I was twelve.

Each time I visited, his quiff would be salted with more grey hairs, his body softer around the middle. He was the embodiment of 'Dad' in a cable-knit jumper and sheepskin slippers, dispensing clumsy hugs and forcing fivers on me that I never thought to refuse. He was insubstantial for ten years, a voice at the end of a phone line.

At the age of twenty-nine, after two unfinished university degrees, years of jobs that wore the guise of a career and a wedding day filled with sweat-stained white satin and my love's denim-blue eyes, I had a baby.

On the day of my son's birth my father became solid again. I watched as he lowered himself onto the edge of the hospital bed inch by careful inch, as if afraid his newly regained mass would break it. Dad lifted his finger until it hovered over the downy, wrinkled brow, and when the tiny fist grasped it as if to hold him there forever, a tear dropped from Dad's grey cheek onto skin no more than two hours old. He became the one to call when *Baa Baa Black Sheep* threatened to steal my sanity, the one who would push the pram around the docks, throwing clumps of desiccated white sliced to the swans, while I sank gratefully into an hour of Quality Street and soap operas. He was no longer the Vanishing Man and though I knew I would never see him fully-rounded, that there were parts of him that would always be missing for me, I was glad my son would have the cave-bear to protect him as he grew.

After years of solidity Dad began to disappear again. First to go was the part that had spent hours building sand castles on the endless span of Weston beach when I was six, the part of him that smoothed the turrets and picked out arrow slits with a discarded chip fork and was more bereft than I was when the sea devoured it all.

Next to vanish was the ribbon that held back my hair on my cousin Rachel's wedding day. Back then he had run the satin between his fingers, telling me it was the colour of leprechaun's gold, the colour of an owl's eyes but only one that hunts in the day. The parts of him that began to disappear seemed inconsequential and unimportant. The Dad-shaped man remained so we just got on with making tea, hanging out the washing, or watching our own children grow away from us. The fact there was less of him was surely a natural part of growing old?

Then one day the part of him that knew my birthday was gone. I don't know when it vanished exactly, sometime between Easter and the May bank holiday. Someone had taken an eraser and wiped away a whole section of his life, of our life, and I, a child again, was wounded, angry it was me he wouldn't remember. I curled in on myself, a woodlouse in my tight shell and wondered why it was me and not the others. Why was I the part of him that was so easy to lose? It felt like rejection, expulsion, the branding of a difference that I'd not known existed. After days and weeks I uncurled my armour plating and rejoined the family. But though we all knew he was fading we continued with our lives. What else was there to do?

One day my father and I were walking together along the beach, over the very sand that he did not remember transforming into castles. The sky was filled with inflated, grey clouds and the sea reflected their colour. I walked ahead then turned to watch him hobble alone. I noticed his gait had changed, that one trouser leg dragged damply through the sandy puddles. At first I thought he'd hit a patch of mud that was sucking at him, drawing him down below the worm casts and splinters of shell. Then it struck me, his right foot was gone just below the ankle.

When I was small I had noticed that foot lagged behind him when he walked, I thought it dawdling and lazy because it dragged the ground and scuffed the toe of every shoe it wore. It was the foot that had been smashed decades earlier in a motorcycle accident. Now all evidence of the accident was gone. I asked him where the foot was but he was unsure.

'It must be somewhere. I'll have put it down to keep it safe.'

We never found it and it was not missed, by him at least. Along with it had gone the throbbing pains on winter mornings and the scars like pale ladders that scaled his shin and calf. But *I* missed it. The scars had been part of him and now he was a lesser man through losing them.

After the troublesome foot, other parts of him vanished. Some suddenly, as if stolen in the night, others fading, growing paler as the days progressed until it seemed as if they had never been. First was the hand that took my mother's on their wedding day, that helped fix the puncture on my first bicycle, that gave a black eye to the man who mugged my Nan for her pension. Then the shoulders vanished that had carried me squealing with delight under the low-hanging elder blossom, only for the two of us to emerge from the tunnel of branches showered with tiny white stars.

He lost the knee that had been my cantering horse, bearing me to Banbury Cross. My mother lost the knee that bent, uncertain of the response, to bestow the chip of diamond in the cheap velvet box. I loved that knee, those shoulders, but my love didn't stop them disappearing.

The day I watched his lips dart away, flapping like a wrinkled, rose-tinted butterfly, was the day that broke my heart. They took with them every kiss planted on my bruised knees or my tear-stained cheeks, every tuneless whistle and bite through plump brown sausages and soft white bread. They took with them what it was to be my dad: the sarcasm and the dodgy, dated jokes, the exasperating sermons delivered with good intentions.

There came a day when there was nothing left of him. Even his heart had slunk away, hiding itself somewhere dark and dank and secret, taking with it his love for us all.

Standing alone on the beach, on the first day after the world was empty of him, I believed he was gone forever and I was at a loss what to mourn the most; the fact that he was gone or that we had known each other for such a short time. Or that after decades, there was so little I knew of him and so many questions I hadn't thought to ask. Now there was not a scrap of him left for me to grieve over, just me and the waves licking at the sand.

I wriggled my toes in the wash and imagined him, intact again, his bare feet leaving deep prints to fill with sparkling foam. I closed my eyes and listened. I heard the wind buffeting my ears, the mocking cry of a gull … and music, only snatches at first, and then a whole phrase, fragile, torn by the breeze. I heard a song I half-remembered, one Dad used to conjure from dusty vinyl to crackle through the house, battling the smell of roast meat for supremacy. A soft, sad clarinet described the melody and I was left breathless, shattered by the vision of childhood Sundays, a yearning for a time that's gone. I felt vulnerable, as if my dad-shaped wound had laid my pain on view for all to see.

Then another sound twined around the tune; a man's whistle, struggling to sustain the notes, mimicking the warble of the reed. The name of the tune came to me, a painful bolt from my childhood: *Strangers on the Shore*. I opened my eyes and Dad was there beside me. He was only a shadow, or the flicker of a shadow, but grew more solid as the music went on. He took my hand and I cried and we danced, our toes scuffing the sand, scuffing each other, until giggling and breathless he released me and left me to dance alone.

Now I often walk along the beach and I'll whistle that same tune and for a time he comes back to me and we smile together. I hold his hand and we whistle, one to the other, until the song is over and he's gone. But for two minutes fifty-one seconds he is solid and I can feel the calluses on his palms and his bristles against my cheek. The music brings him back to me.

And he's my Dad again.

Journey's End

Sandy Hashimi

Violet didn't consider the driver of the vehicle to be a killer, well not unless he had been drinking of course. But who was to say, he didn't stop to be breathalysed. Perhaps Buzz was depressed at losing his once luxurious black fur, or bored with eating the same old dinner every night (the vet said the unappetising little brown pebbles prevented cystitis). Perhaps he thought it was better to go quickly than to start leaking, suffer painful joints and forget which side of the road your dinner bowl lived. This was something Violet had some sympathy with. Suicide or accident, one thing was certain, Violet wasn't responsible and it certainly should not mean she was unfit to own another feline friend. Indeed, this had been at the very hub of the latest argument with Stephen and Richard.

'I don't think that's a good idea.'

And had she asked for her eldest son's opinion?

'You don't want to be bothered with all that palaver, not at your age!' chimed in Richard.

And when Violet had actually tried to say, yes it was a grand notion, and yes she did want the fuss and bother to keep her busy and looking after another living creature was just the thing, her sons had already busied themselves with packing away the little china owls from the sideboard into one of the ominous cardboard boxes littering the floor.

Thinning out. That's what they'd called it when it started a few months ago. Like her house was a choked vegetable plot and the inedible bits needed pulling, and she had wondered then where all this weeding would end.

Looking back, Violet realised that's when it started; the death of her furry twelve-year-old companion had heralded all this decluttering, the beginning of what she now called their Grand Plan. She realised they must have been waiting for the cat to die, like a couple of feline reapers, all cavernous eye sockets and wide jaws hidden behind their benevolent middle-aged mugs. She suspected if the hit and run motorist hadn't achieved their goal, they might have thought up ways of committing felicide themselves. She had even asked them their whereabouts on the night of the accident, surreptitiously of course, as if she was genuinely interested in their mundane lives.

'Less clutter will lessen the chance of you tripping over something,' Stephen explained, in a slightly loud tone as if there was something wrong with her hearing. But as she had no intention of going for a stroll on the top shelf of the dresser she was more than a little suspicious. Besides, she had lived in the house for forty years and knew where every single item was placed. She could navigate her home in the inky dark, which was increasingly necessary for the nightly loo runs and she had never tripped over anything yet. Except once. But that was the cat's fault and he soon forgave her his airborne whizz to the bottom of the stairs.

No, Violet knew what all this tidying meant. She hadn't

spent eighty-seven years on this planet without learning a thing or two. Her two sons might have important jobs and drive expensive cars and go on exotic holidays with their insipid wives and vacuous children (all except one – Samantha was a good girl) but they were dealing with someone who had survived Hitler, Harold Wilson and the Daleks for goodness sake.

They thought she hadn't twigged the real purpose behind the Sunday afternoon drives into the country. Outings she tried to persuade them she didn't enjoy and would much rather have spent the time at home with Tom, and of course Buzz before he shook paws with an unforgiving bumper. Yes, of course she remembered Tom was dead! That didn't mean her husband's memory wasn't in every corner of the house. Whose business was it if she occasionally set an extra plate at the dinner table, or if she sometimes called one of them by their late father's name? She knew neither of them were actually her husband – for one thing they didn't have such good teeth nor were they in possession of a decent arse between them.

A hot, stuffy leather-come-lemon-smelling car trip was not Violet's idea of a treat. Sitting in her favourite armchair doing one of her crosswords, when she could find a damn pen, now that was much better. The slowing down as they passed some Victorian house and the occasional glimpse of a nodding head sat on a bench in the sunshine or another white-haired figure shuffling across a tailored lawn, usually led to one of them saying, 'Looks nice doesn't it, Mum?' And she had learned to agree, because that meant they would look at each other in a self-satisfied way and take her home.

They were as transparent as the skin on the back of her brown-spotted hand, but a deal less attractive in her opinion. But this decluttering had really got on her nerves and sitting in her denuded living room, all her knickknacks in boxes in the spare room, the seeds of a cunning counter-plan began to sprout and Violet was sure if she could concentrate on it for long enough she could foil their Grand Plan. And get what her heart desired.

Although Violet hadn't realised it at the time, it was Sylvia's endless wittering at the bingo afternoons that had sown the germ of an idea.

'I can't hear the bloody caller,' she warned her neighbour who insisted on talking throughout the games.

'No dear, can't bear him either. Is he Indian?'

And so it had gone on, and on. Then, because once you had tried all ways to shut the silly woman up (including calling House! when you didn't actually have one, just for the thirty seconds stunned silence it evoked), Violet had no choice but to listen to her.

It took a while to prepare, but all great schemes require careful planning and eventually Violet found writing notes meant she could focus her mind much better. She wasn't sure if she was forgetting things, or if she simply hadn't thought of them in the first place, but she didn't want a repeat of the embarrassment of being walked home by the surfing shop's patron when she had tried to book a shampoo and set. And why would you call such a place *The Permanent Wave* for goodness sake, if it wasn't to entice customers in for a curl?

However, had she written down the name of her hairdressing salon it would never have happened, she saw that now.

By the time they had driven slowly past Journey's End, for that was the name of the place, on three consecutive Sundays, Violet realised the boys had found their target, reassured as they were by their mother's seeming enthusiasm. She also suspected the final step of their Grand Plan was scheduled for the following weekend's car trip about which Stephen had hinted.

'We thought we might take a look inside that nice old house next Sunday, Mum. What do you think?'

'Lovely, dear,' she gushed. Over my dead body you conniving sods, she thought, and when they had gone she double checked her notes to ensure the counter-plan was ready to roll.

Preparations hadn't been all smooth sailing. Richard had this bizarre habit of checking the cupboards and fridge whenever he visited, as if she might be hiding something.

'I'm looking for inspiration,' he explained.

Once he found her purse tucked between the Special K and the Porridge Oats and Violet congratulated herself on discombobulating her youngest son, although she couldn't quite remember coming up with the idea. Lately he was very concerned about the amount of prawns she seemed to be buying.

'I like prawns,' she explained matter-of-factly.

'Yes, but do you really want to eat them every day? Besides, if not properly prepared you know how dangerous seafood can be.'

Not properly prepared! Who did he think he was speaking to? Hadn't she properly prepared all manner of meals for the last sixty-five years? Hadn't he and his brother grown into six foot something streaks of shite because of her grand cooking?

'I like prawns,' she repeated. Prawns were an integral part of the counter-plan and were being successfully pressed into service on a daily basis.

The next Sunday the two men arrived at their usual time. As they walked up the path to the front door they weren't too concerned that the curtains were still drawn together. Their mother often complained the light bothered their late father's eyes when he was trying to watch the TV in the front room. They were reassured when they noted that none of their mother's collection of porcelain owls had found their way back onto every conceivable surface, or that the gas cooker had been left on. They assumed she was pottering in the garden or upstairs getting dressed. When they realised the house was deserted they thought she might well have lost track of the day and gone down to the Co-op to buy yet more bloody prawns, but half an hour later they had to admit something wasn't right. A hurried search of the house revealed the absence of a small suitcase, a few clothes and toiletries, two framed photographs (neither containing pictures of them) and the old cat basket.

In the meantime Violet was settling into her new abode. It wasn't like her proper home, but it would have to do.

'Home is where the heart is,' she purred at Buzz 2, who had been reborn into a stray tabby cat with a missing eye and a penchant for prawns. She set about hanging up her few clothes and putting out the toiletries on the ugly white dressing table. She unpacked the supplies into the larder and fridge – including the prawns – which she sniffed first to reassure herself that she wasn't going to poison her new best friend.

Sylvia had come up trumps and even though she was a habitual chatterer, Violet would miss their weekly bingo games. She didn't suppose she could continue with that little outing now she was living in Sylvia's daughter's house! Violet was no stranger to squatting. At the end of the war, before she married, she and some student friends had actually squatted in a prefab of questionable stability for nearly a year. It had been very exciting, and Violet's dormant sense of adventure had reawakened when Sylvia had explained her daughter was spending a sabbatical in New Zealand, leaving her little terrace house alone and unloved and with a front door key hanging on a hook in the shed.

The counter-plan had worked. The careful collection of provisions, the enticing of Buzz 2 with tasty prawns from where he had taken to spraying her gladioli and a taxi-drive were all it had required. And she had taken not one, but three different taxis just to get to her new home; a journey of some twelve miles, ending up only six doors away from her own house. She could actually see her sons park the petrol guzzling car, with no thought of rationing for goodness sake, their dark heads close together as they conspired all the way up the brick path and into her house. Half an hour later they retraced their steps wearing confused expressions, pausing at the gate to look back at the empty house as if they might find their mother abseiling down the facade. Gotcha, she thought, as she shared a prawn sandwich with her furry mate.

Violet might have remained undiscovered had she been familiar with Sylvia's daughter's new-fangled cooker. Try as she might, she couldn't get the hob to light and after a couple of days food was becoming a problem. Eating raw mince was very satisfying for Buzz 2 but did not suit Violet's palate. When she tried to prepare it in the microwave contraption, she nuked it to a gritty gravel and didn't enjoy the arcing firework display that the gold-rimmed plate sparked through the little glass door. It occurred to Violet that her counter-plan had not taken account of the variables that were now dogging her new life. She would need to have a rethink.

She sat behind the net curtains and watched the comings and goings outside her old house, with Buzz 2 curled up on her lap. She was quite shocked to see the police arrive, Stephen and Richard trailing behind them, no trace of the self-satisfied expressions on their grey faces. The stab of remorse Violet felt hadn't lasted more than a couple of minutes before she was worrying if those men in their heavy boots had wiped their feet, or what poor Tom might make of it all. He wasn't keen on strangers in the house. After that the police disappeared, and for two more days no-one came or went. Had she learned how to use the remote control for the 36 inch LCD television, Violet would have seen she had become quite the local celebrity.

It occurred to her that she could remain hidden and do her washing, cooking and say hello to Tom, provided she visited her old house under cover of darkness. She didn't think this was a crime; it was her house, she had the key, but nevertheless she thought it prudent to be covert because squatting might well still be illegal. The final decision to visit her old house was reached while doing a spot of ironing (not hers, this was in a pile in the lean-to, and Violet hated ironing piles whomever they belonged to). Later, as she waited in her old familiar kitchen for the washing to finish, as she stirred the chicken soup, as she assured herself Tom was still in residence, she heard the sirens.

Once Stephen and Richard hugged her and assured themselves she was unharmed, there was some serious telling off and even the murmured threat of ending her days in a prison cell. Violet thought this a little extreme – after all, hadn't Sylvia's daughter gained a whole pile of freshly-pressed clothes and only lost an ironing board cover, before the neighbours heard the squeal of the smoke alarm and called the fire brigade? However, Violet took the route of least resistance and agreed she had indeed been very unwise, and she certainly wouldn't do it again, particularly as some people seem to have cookers that can't be lit, televisions that don't turn on and are incapable of keeping on top of their ironing.

Violet now has a room on the South West corner of Journey's End. The triple mirrors on the little oak dressing table multiply the collection of porcelain owls and she has her own television with a remote control she understands and a whole selection of pens to hand. Buzz 2, with the missing eye and a newly-acquired fear of ironing boards has been allowed to stay but he sleeps downstairs in the conservatory, rarely sees a prawn and isn't allowed into the residents' rooms. Nevertheless he's a popular member of the community, curling up on laps in the day room and guarding the flower beds. It isn't so bad, even if some of the residents are a little doolally in Violet's opinion. But she doesn't have to remember to turn off the gas, her clothes are always nicely pressed, the hairdresser visits every fortnight and none of the old people chatter through the bingo games.

And, best of all, Tom decided to come as well.

GRANBO

Paul Stephenson

Dementia ... I will always remember when I first heard this word. Well, I'd heard it before, but it held no real meaning until the day I walked in on my mother and Aunt Jeannie talking in Nan's kitchen. They fell silent as soon as they saw me, but from their teary eyes and the numerous empty mugs on the kitchen table, I knew I'd walked in on a serious discussion.

'Where's Nan?' I asked, although from their faces I already knew the answer.

'Sit down, Ray,' my mother said and I sank onto the chair nearest me without taking my eyes from hers.

'What's happened? Where's Nan?' I asked again, and I could feel the warmth drain from my face.

The discussion that followed was one that I will never forget. Nan had 'an episode' as my Aunt called it, and had been taken to hospital. It turned out that on her way home from the bingo hall she had gotten on the wrong bus and had ended up all the way on the other side of town, but had no recollection of where she was, or how she got there. The bus driver had called for an ambulance when she had started to panic and at the hospital they had diagnosed the early signs of Alzheimer's.

What my mother and Aunt Jeannie were discussing, before I had walked in on them, was whether or not to put her in a care home. My mother's idea, it turned out, and Aunt Jeannie was against it. She knew, as I did, there was no way Nan would agree to it, but they said there was no alternative unless one of them quit their job and moved in to look after her.

'What about me?' I said frowning, shocked that neither of them had considered me as Nan's carer. I was always calling in to see her anyway. 'I'm not working at the minute, and I'm gonna lose my flat anyway … I can't afford to keep it on.'

They didn't voice it, but I could see from the wary glances between them that they didn't think I'd be up to it. However, my offer freed them of a difficult decision, so it was agreed upon and I moved in that very day, to be there when she came home from hospital.

Nan seemed fine when she walked through the door with my Uncle Sean, and her face lit up like Blackpool illuminations when my mother told her I had moved in.

'Wanna cup of tea, Nan?' I asked, an uncontrollable smile splitting my face in two, as it always did upon seeing her.

'Sit yaself down lad,' she said, waving a dismissive hand in the air. 'I'll make my own. I'm not too old 'n' daft to boil a kettle yet.'

It went on this way for months. Everything I offered to do for her was met with refusal, and she wound up looking after *me*. I felt a little guilty about this, but it made her happy, so what could I do? I didn't even see what all the fuss about Alzheimer's was … until later.

It all began on that Thursday morning ...

6:30 a.m. and she was awake. The kettle clicked its steamed conclusion and the toaster popped its wholemeal, heavily-seeded 'It's good for you ... Shurrup an' earrit,' breakfast addition. I could hear the pan sizzle with the expectation of eggs fried (mmm, nutmeg) to perfection and heard the raspy crunch of Nan's heavy hand smearing the blueberry jam.

'Yes Nan, I'm up!' I called, although she had not yet called me down for breakfast. 'Supermarket today, remember?'

'Post office too,' she reminded me ... Dementia, my hairy, white arse!

Now shops, supermarkets especially, and my Nan have never seen eye to eye. Even after the need to do so had been removed by an improved benefits system, she still lived in a time where 'Wherever a meal could be snatched, it should be!'

'Nan,' I'd say, 'get that out your bag! We can afford it.'

'Oh f'off!' she'd reply. 'No-one's a-peeping.'

Some days, nothing would convince her of her misconduct. All I could do was mask her blatant thievery by jokingly joining in, picking up items, hiding them in my coat and then putting them back before the security guards could spot us and haul us off to be searched.

Sometimes she was fine. She wandered through the aisles, picking what was needed, placing her choices in the basket, walking to the checkout, and not even acknowledge the glares of the 'Failed copper, turned bully' as she paid for every item.

This Thursday was not one of those placid, uneventful days. I watched her like a kestrel eyes a mouse in the long

81

grass. I wasn't embarrassed by it. I had become immune to it over the months, but it could be annoying. Here's me, a twenty-four year old man strutting through the aisles, stubble on chin, winking to the more attractive women shoppers, and all the while, watching for my own Grandmother's illegality.

This is where it all becomes confusing for me, dementia that is. To look at her whenever I caught her, swag in hand, ready to be stashed away in that old tan, leather handbag, to see her eyes light up behind her glasses, dart left and right, and watch her tweed clad shoulders hunch and the wicked grin plump her cheeks and squint her eyes, like she knew exactly what she was doing … It lit me up inside every time. Did just then, writing the words.

This day, she seemed really out of sorts. She stood in the tinned foods aisle, bewildered, looking this way and that.

'Ray, where's the toothpaste?' she asked.

'It's three aisles down, Nan. We've just been there; we bought soap, remember?'

'I, I don't … can't …'

'It's okay Nan. Stay here, I'll go get it.' I walked off down the aisle, a hand on my jaw to keep it from trembling. My eyes began to well up and my heart felt like an old, punctured ball, deflated in my chest.

We finished the shopping at my Nan's usual pace. At the checkout she smiled a cheeky grin to the stick-thin store guard, who, in my opinion had no place in the security trade – I'd coughed up scarier things than him. Unknown to me at this point, was that she'd swiped three large tins of sweetcorn while I was looking for the toothpaste. Why the hell she pinched sweetcorn was anyone's guess. There was only my brother, Wayne, who would ever ask for it, and he was serving six months in prison for aggravated burglary. I thought about returning the tins, but the hassle didn't seem worth it.

The post office was only a short walk down from High Street, on the corner of Luke's Lane by the butcher shop, but it took us ten minutes to get there. Nan was not as spritely as she used to be and it took her an age to get anywhere on foot.

The queue was six people out of the door. A light rain started and neither of us had remembered her brolly.

'Maybe we should wait in the bus shelter, Nan?' I suggested. 'Just until this rain eases off.'

'You soft sod,' she replied. 'It's barely even spitting, and you know the queue'll only get longer. I'm not waiting till tomorrow for my money.'

I couldn't argue with her ... Well, I could have, but it wouldn't have made any difference. Nan joined the queue. I held back and lit up a smoke while she chatted with a few old women she recognised from the bingo hall.

'Eeeee, did you hear about Gladys?' Nan said over the rumble-hum of a passing bus. 'Five thousand pound and she only bought three cards ... It's always the same ones that win; I'm sure it's bloody rigged!'

'I think you've got summit there, Sam,' came the reply from a hunched old lady with strangely blue hair, who could barely crane her neck to look up at Nan. 'I'm sure that bingo caller's her fancy man.'

This idle chit-chat went on until they finally went into the post office. I stamped out the remainder of my smoke on the pavement, picked up the butt and walked over to the bin. My intention was to wait outside for her, but when I saw *him* join the short queue outside, twitchy and watchful, I knew he was up to no good. He was about my age, a little shorter, dressed all in black: tracksuit bottoms, hooded top, woollen hat. The epitome, in my view, of a wrong-un.

I watched every twitch and glance he made, ready to be over there in seconds. I expected him to dip his hands into the bag of the old lady in front of him, but he didn't. The customers continued to exit the post office and I grew increasingly nervous as I watched him near the entrance.

I pulled out another cigarette, but before I even got out my lighter, I threw it to the ground and approached the door.

'Excuse me, please,' I said to the old lady standing before him.

'Hey,' the mock burglar said, 'there's a queue here you know?'

I ignored him and continued inside. Nan was standing over by the serving windows, still chatting away about this or that, and when I approached she turned, beaming that mischievous grin of hers.

'This is our Ray,' she said, pinching my cheek and forcing the stubble back into my face. 'Isn't he a handsome lad?'

Old blue hair smiled up at me nodding her head. I felt uncomfortable, my face hot and itchy, but I returned the smile.

'How old's your Sandra now?' Nan asked, clapping a hand onto her shoulder and almost knocking her to the floor. 'Maybe we should introduce them?'

'Sandra?' Old Blue replied, unfazed by her near brush with

sprawling to the tiled floor. 'Don't know any Sandra ... d'you mean Susan?'

'Yes, Susan, that's her. You'll have to excuse my missing marbles.'

'Well, she'll be, erm ... forty-six this year ... how old are you this year, Ray?'

'I'm twenty-four!' I said, wanting more than anything to get the hell out of there.

'Well,' Old Blue began, 'I think you're a bit young for our ...' She trailed off, her eyes left mine and looked past me. Her smile faltered.

'Everyone stay where you are.' The shout came from behind me and I turned to see the man in black pull an old, rusted kitchen knife from under his hooded top. 'If everyone does as they're told then no-one'll get hurt.'

I was stunned, unable to move. Not five minutes before, I was ready to punch seven shades of snot out of him if he touched that old lady's bag. Now I stood as wide eyed and terrified as everybody else. Well, almost everybody.

'Wayne!' Nan shrieked. 'Just what the hell do you think you're doing?'

She began towards him and I grabbed her arm. 'Nan, that's not our Wayne! Wayne's in prison.'

'He bloody well will be if he keeps going on like this!' she said and pulled free from my grasp. I wanted to go after her, but I couldn't move and something inside me reasoned that even the nastiest of rogues wouldn't hurt an old lady.

'Give me the knife, Wayne,' she ordered, standing toe to toe, as tall as he was, glaring her disapproval right into him.

The man in black simply fixed his gaze with hers, grinned and said, 'Sod off, you daft old bag.'

She didn't even flinch. His grin faded.

'Get back over there,' he ordered, pointing with the knife, 'or I swear I'll take this knife and ...'

He didn't have a chance to finish.

'Talk to *me* like that, will you?' I'd never seen her so angry. 'You ungrateful little shit!'

I want to say this is as fast as I'd ever seen her move, but I don't remember seeing her move. All I remember is seeing him fall back, crack his head on the outer window and sprawl to the floor, dazed, with blood seeping from a small cut in his temple.

Everyone in the post office cheered, except me. I ran over to Nan and grasped her arms.

'Nan, are ... are you okay?' My face was flushed and my legs quivered with unused adrenaline.

'Better than him,' she said, lifting up her bag and patting where the tins sat dented inside, 'I bet he's not too fond of sweetcorn anymore.'

'Nan,' I said, 'what were you thinking? You, you could have been killed. That's *not* our Wayne.'

She looked down to the bleeding, groaning man as two of the elderly gents from the queue held him down and another kicked the knife skidding across the floor away from him. Nan turned to me, pushed her glasses back up her nose, smiled and winked.

Did she know all along? Was it all part of some devious

misdirection to get him to drop his guard? I never found out. She never talked about it, just continued on afterwards as she always had. Even the police, when they asked for a statement were met with a wall of misunderstanding, not that she'd have given them what they wanted even if she did remember.

My Nan ... she was hard as nails!

Wish You Were Here

Viki Birchall

I heaved the silver Samsonite suitcase onto the hideously patterned bedspread. Like the suitcase, the bed was far too big. I would struggle to find a suitable depression in the mattress without the obstacle of your body to rest against.

I had intended to dump the information given to us on the bus from the airport into the nearest bin, but for some reason it was still peeking hopefully from my holdall, promising much fun and pleasure, although not of the kind that Jason and Sean would have approved, had I given in and let them come with me. The travel rep had recommended a trip to the nearby old town of Teguise, citing its historic charms and weekly local market. I made a note to pop to the desk and make a reservation after dinner, if only so that I could laze about on the beach for the remainder of the holiday. Then I rang your mobile, hoping to hear your voice.

I had to be satisfied with your voicemail.

'Hi, this is Florry Makepeace. I'm not here right now, so please leave a message.'

I hung up, satisfied with the image of your mobile charging on the hall table.

Despite the restaurant's size I had to wait twenty minutes for a table, hastily cleared of its contents, but still containing a pattern of crumbs and colourful stains. The push and shove to grab the last plate, the last few chips, the last hard lump of battered fish pretty much put paid to any notion that I might have had about a peaceful first night. I ignored my longing for a beer.

The meal didn't improve with the intrusion of another diner clad in ill-fitting shiny trousers, a lace top and bearing a too-bright smile.

'Y'orite, luv? You don't mind me sitting here, d'you? Only, the place is packed and the *camarero* over there said I'd 'ave to wait. Fifteen bloody minutes! Anyway, I thought you might appreciate the company. Me name's Bonny. Suits me, don't ya think?'

Bonny, and the name definitely didn't suit her, plonked her handbag beneath the table without waiting for any response.

'You just arrived, luv? You're as pale as milk. Need some sun, you do. What's yer name anyway, and what's a handsome chap like you doing here by himself?'

I was tempted to tell her that I was trying, unsuccessfully, to avoid any kind of company. What I actually said was, 'Oh, um, you know, just, um, ah ...'

The waiter's appearance with a notepad and an enquiring glance hastened my escape from a disastrous episode of awkward prevarication.

'Were you gonna get some wine, luv? I'll share yours with you. Bottle of red, please, *camarero*.'

The waiter gestured at me with a pad and pen in hand, 'Your room number, *señor*.'

'Erm.' For some reason I felt nervous rather than chagrined

at having to give my room number for a bottle of wine that I didn't want. 'Three three seven. And a small bottle of water for me. Thanks.'

The wine and water were brought and dispensed surprisingly quickly. I admired the efficiency of the staff, although in hindsight all they seemed to do was run about the place carrying bottles of the house red or pints of frothy lager for thirsty guests.

'You don't want any wine? All the more for me, then. I hope you're gonna keep me company while I drink it. After all, I have saved you from being by yoursel' at dinner, have I not? So, your name, luv?'

'Oh, it's Ben. Ben Makepeace.'

'Bonny and Ben! We sound like a pair of comedy characters!' Bonny guffawed at this. Guffawed: a word I'd only ever read in the Beano, and never really known what it meant, until then. People in all directions were staring at us. I found myself counting her fillings rather than meet any of those glances.

'Well, Ben, I see you've eaten. I'll just go and get myself something. Don't go anywhere.'

From behind, a bright red thong was visible through obscenely tight trousers. Her black top had no back, and the strap of a matching red bra was cutting into a puffy expanse of peeling skin. Tattooed wings looked desperate to take flight, although whether they belonged to a fairy or a fire-breathing dragon it was hard to tell. In comparison to the vivid and meticulous Japanese designs with which you chose to decorate your fabulous body, this was a misguided attempt to be different, like everybody else.

Believe me, Florry, I did consider leaving right then, but I knew you'd insist that I said goodbye properly and give her some strong indication that I'd prefer my own company in future. That would be the grown-up thing to do.

A plate of pizza slices landed on the table, followed by Bonny's fat bosom.

'Well it's been a long day, Bonny. I'm exhausted. I hope you'll excuse me …'

'Don't be daft luv,' Bonny interjected without looking up from her first slice of soggy margherita. 'Sit yoursel' down. There's a singer on shortly. Some tribute act to the *Ladies of Country*, the poster says. Tammy Wynette, Dolly Parton, all that.'

Bonny belted out a few lines from some country song that I vaguely remembered hearing as a child, attracting more glances. Unabashed, she giggled once again, wiggling her shoulders in time to the music playing in her head. I spent the remainder of the time it took her to finish her pizza trying in vain to come up with an excuse to leave.

Two hours or so later, as Bonny wiped the muddy mess from under her eyes at the last bar of *Stand By Your Man* I stood to bid her farewell, already mentally rearranging my plans for the following evening. An earlier meal followed by a very early night would be perfect, I thought (although I'd never admit that to the lads).

After a night of light sleep, rolling into other people's body shapes, I was shocked into wakefulness by the telephone.

'Y'orite, luv? It's Bonny. Are you comin' down to brekkie, or what? I thought we could do it together, then head down to the beach.'

'I'm not really hungry,' I improvised, not entirely surprised that she had memorised my room number. 'Besides, I'd planned to go shopping today.' Damn! I had planned to book the trip, but by the time I'd managed to get away from Bonny the rep had been long gone.

'Oh, lovely. I love shopping. I tell you what, meet me in the lobby in half an hour and I'll come with you. How's about that, eh?' The phone went dead.

After the shopping trip, where I bought you a silk scarf in your favourite shade of purple, I managed to avoid Bonny by heading to the restaurant early, hiding in the centre of the protective huddle that muttered and squeezed forward in anticipation of the doors opening. The food was a damn sight fresher and the table linen clean and bright at this hour, but to experience it I had to sacrifice a couple of hours of sunshine followed by a peach sunset that the travel rep had promised would melt right into the sea. Still, I had escaped that overpowering Northern drawl and the sweet vomit-smell of perfume. And my wallet was given a break. After a reasonable meal I headed to the lifts, looking forward to an evening reading a gory thriller in my boxers.

'Ben, luv, over 'ere.'

I turned to see her standing at the notice board with two much younger women. They were dressed in similar brightly striped dresses and flip-flops, each of them carrying large wicker shoulder bags.

'Girls, this is Ben who I was telling you about. Ben, this is Sam and Donna. I met them on the beach this afternoon. I was hoping you'd come down, but I suppose you were recovering from our shopping trip, eh? They're lovely girls, Ben. I'm sure we'll have a fabulous time.'

'Will you? Lovely.'

'Not you. We. *We'll* have a good time. I've put your name down for this trip to Graciosa Island tomorrow. It's a volcano, or something. But they give you free Sangria and Paella when you get there and that lovely travel rep, Sebastian with the tight buns, is going to be the guide. So if you just pay the rep there we'll be done and we can go and have a little drink.'

Excuses fought for attention inside my head, but unfortunately none of them were brave enough to be heard. That Sebastian 'with the tight buns' clearly had me pegged as one of his kind, when I thought back to the sidelong pouts he was giving me on the bus from the airport.

My shoulders sagged and my wallet honestly groaned aloud as I paid two hundred Euros for four tickets for a trip that I didn't want to take. With company that I'd rather not have had.

'Come on, Ben. Let's get a drink to celebrate. Cocktails all round. Mine's a Pina Colada.' Then followed an excruciating chorus of some cheesy, vaguely familiar song, seemingly about her favourite cocktail.

I cringed as I avoided Bonny's hips, jutting in my direction. Sam and Donna had bemused expressions, obviously not recognising a tune that had been forgotten years before they were born.

'Yes, make mine a brandy. A double,' I announced. Bang went my evening with a cup of tea and my own company, but sometimes escape is simply impossible.

Bonny was loudly irritating, and an expensive inconvenience to boot. It horrified me to think that the other hotel guests would assume that I was her toy boy, as she squashed onto the sofa next to me. But between her and the two girls I did manage to almost enjoy myself. Sam told us about her job as an assistant to the Human Resources Manager at a large chain of supermarkets. We groaned and laughed in equal measure at her stories of staff misfortunes and hilariously unsuccessful job interviews.

Donna was equally entertaining and, by the time the three women decided to annoy the restaurant staff by taking a table five minutes before closing time, I'd even forgotten to care about the sideways glances of the other drinkers of the bar as we screeched and giggled unselfconsciously throughout the evening.

I awoke the next day with a pain in my skull and a constant urge to vomit. I knew that getting out of bed was out of the question, so the women would have to go on the trip without me. I hadn't experienced a hangover like this one since my teens, despite the amount of alcohol that I used to put away with the lads every Friday, until recently. Looking back, the last time I had been drunk was last Christmas when Lucy and Dave had come over and we'd played Twister. We were so drunk we fell and knocked over the Christmas tree. Even the Boxing Day hangover was fine, you waking me up with wet kisses and a warm hand from behind. But this ringing wake up call was less welcoming.

'… Hello?'

'Ben, luv, we're on the bus. I've told the driver he has to wait, so get your backside down here now. I've saved you a seat next to me.'

I hung up to the repeated bars of *Why are we waiting?* in the background. Great, a day with two desperate overweight girls and a horny grandma. Just what I needed.

The final day arrived after a week of failing miserably to avoid Bonny. After breakfast I wandered down to the beach. Noticing Bonny's fat leopard-print handbag next to a pink towel, I headed another hundred yards or so along the sand and found a spot on the other side of the lifeguards' hut. Pulling my cap over my eyes, I lay back to relax. Peace, at last.

I was startled awake by thuds from the hut. Sitting up, I watched the man in too-tight red shorts and yellow polo shirt race towards the sea, where people were shouting and waving next to a stationary pedalo. Irrationally I glanced to where Bonny's still-empty pink towel lay. Unthinkingly I dashed to the water, flailing uselessly towards all the commotion.

'You were too bastard close, you silly English bastards!' accused a Spanish man holding a bat and ball. Meanwhile, the lifeguard had lifted someone out of the sea and was effortlessly rushing back to the sand with them in his arms, leaping over the shallow waves. People were starting to disperse, apart from the worried pedalo people, who appeared to be waiting for someone to tell them what to do.

I went back to the beach and watched the lifeguard talking to Bonny, checking for signs of concussion.

'I'm alright, love. Honest. It was a shock, that's all. Look, here's my friend, Ben.'

The crowd of onlookers made way for me, as I knelt next to her. The lifeguard looked me over and ordered me to bring her straight to the lifeguards' station if she started to feel unwell.

As I accompanied her back to her belongings, Bonny clinging onto me, said, 'Oh Ben, my life flashed before me. I thought I was going to meet my Raymond. I miss him so much.' Tears rolled down her cheeks and a huge intake of breath preceded a violent expulsion of wet sobs. She turned into my chest and I smoothed her clotted hair. Instead of feeling uncomfortable I was overtaken by a surge of sympathy for this poor, irritating wretch.

Afterwards, we enjoyed a last meal together in the a la carte restaurant, my treat. She told me about her husband's stroke last year, and how she was struggling to adjust to being alone after forty years of togetherness. She showed me her tattoo, explaining that the phoenix rising from the ashes symbolised her determination to make a new life for herself, alone. As her Raymond had begged her to do in his final days. And, of course, I told her about you.

I'm sitting now, on our bottom stair, looking at the photograph of you on the side table. I'm going to put this journal and the silk scarf into the drawer and kiss you again. Then Bonny's coming over for tea. She comes once a month and we talk about how we're getting on. I miss you, darling, every day.

A Perfect Maiden Aunt

Hilary Berry

When my Dad's youngest sister, Auntie Doreen, died in 2005, the requiem mass in St Joseph's Church, Bolton, was sparsely attended by a few of her nieces and nephews and two elderly women from the church. As I stood sobbing on the sodden grass of the graveyard, watching the small gathering shiver in the biting October wind, I puzzled over what had happened to my lovely, kind, vivacious aunt. I grieved for the lady she had been and cried for the person she had become nearer to her end.

During the four-hundred mile train journey home to Aberdeen after the funeral, watching fellow passengers busy with laptops and mobile phones, I mused about happier childhood trips on the same line by steam train. My brother Peter and I used to save our pocket money for weeks to buy sweets and lemonade for the nine hour journey from Aberdeen to Manchester each summer holiday. It never seemed to take long, we loved the trip. We usually had a compartment to ourselves and would sit in opposite window seats, savouring the rhythm of the wheels on the track, both absorbed in our colouring books and comics until it was time for the wonderful picnic of lemonade and salmon sandwiches mother packed in her old shopping bag.

On the train journey after the funeral I pictured the Auntie Doreen of my childhood. A tall, slim woman, she always dressed in smart outfits, favouring navy-blue and dusky-pink. Even to go as far as the front gate she would put on her lipstick and tidy her wavy blonde hair. She was very strict with us children about cleaning our teeth and I well remember my neck being scrubbed with the loofah. Despite this she was always kind and summer holidays with my Grandma, Granddad and Auntie Doreen were the highlight of my year. We were city children who blossomed in the delights of fresh air and sunshine. Freed from the constraints of school uniforms and Sunday best we romped all day in shorts and t-shirts in the fields around Grandma's house. This worked up an appetite for Auntie Doreen's wonderful Lancashire hotpot, full of savoury meat and potatoes with a melt-in-your-mouth crust overhanging the edge. Her oven-baked rice pudding with real cream and her warm home-made scones, dripping with butter and blackberry jam, were unbeatable, even by my own mother's standards.

Best of all, I enjoyed the long walks she took us along country lanes and field paths. She never seemed tired after work like our mother and happily took us out each day after tea. I lapped up the country lore she dispensed, discovering the heady fragrance of aptly-named wild flowers: honeysuckle and meadowsweet and the pungency of wild garlic. She knew all the birds by their calls; I heard my first cuckoo on one of her walks. The distinctive two-tone 'cuckoo' sounded delightfully like its namesake clock. Yellowhammers calling, 'a little bit of bread and no cheeeese' were plentiful, and I marvelled at seeing wild birds as bright as canaries. The love of nature she nurtured remained with me all my life.

Each year, a week or so before Christmas, a large parcel would arrive at our house. Peter and I would be in a frenzy of excitement as our mother carefully untied the knots and wound the string into a ball for the 'useful' drawer. The cardboard box beneath contained a multitude of individual presents, all neatly labelled and wrapped in Christmas paper. Peter and I waited for the big day in an agony of anticipation.

As money was always short I don't suppose my parents were able to contribute much to our hopefully-hung stockings. Auntie Doreen's parcel made Christmas for us. I don't remember all she gave us but every year there were colouring books, a new paint set each, boxes of Liquorice Allsorts and tins of toffees. We would be frenzied with delight. Auntie Doreen also remembered our birthdays, usually with a card and a Postal Order for half a crown. Riches indeed!

For the last ten years or so of Auntie Doreen's life, after my parents died, I kept in touch, making the train journey south about twice a year. I sent parcels of thermal underwear at Christmas and stocked up her larder with biscuits and tins of Baxter's Soup while I was there, as she was loath to spend money on food. Not that she showed me any gratitude. Far from it. Auntie Doreen used to criticise me mercilessly.

'Get rid of that skirt,' she'd say. 'It does nothing for you.'

'Have you put more weight on? It wouldn't look so bad if you didn't wear that red sweater.'

I didn't take it too personally as she didn't have a good word to say about anyone else. All her old friends stopped visiting as they grew tired of her rudeness.

Always outspoken and somewhat eccentric, her behaviour seemed to be more bizarre every time I visited. One day her famous rice pudding smelt rather peculiar as it baked. I discovered she had used curry powder instead of cinnamon. She served it up regardless and quite happily ate it.

Concerned about her ability to live alone I began to visit more regularly, sometimes using the overnight bus to go down for a weekend when the train fare was beyond my reach. I was amply repaid. I learned about Doreen's life and our own family history. She used to wake during the night and come through to the living room where I was trying to sleep on the fold-down bed.

'Are you awake, Mary?' she'd ask, using my mother's name. 'I was just thinking about that money I borrowed from Edwin. Did I ever pay him back?'

I was shocked to begin with but learned to go along with what she said and reassure her as far as possible. 'Yes,' I'd say. 'You gave it all back last year. Edwin was very pleased about it.'

'That's good,' she'd reply. 'I just couldn't sleep for thinking about it.'

I realised she was beginning to develop dementia. In common with many other sufferers she was a time traveller, going back to her early years and talking about whatever was important to her at that time. When she mistook me for my mother during the night she often shared important memories with me. We certainly had our share of family secrets; 'Not in front of the children' was strictly observed. I grew up in ignorance of the fact that my Great Uncle James had a wooden leg and my Grandma was blind in one eye.

Some nights Doreen would tell me about her wartime adventures.

'We all had to leave school at fourteen,' she said. 'All of us ended up in Pilkington's cotton mill. It was jolly hard work and you never got the smell of it out of your hair.'

When World War II broke out Doreen had the opportunity to do something new with her life. She left home and journeyed to Plymouth to join the WRNS, mainly because she fancied the uniform and the tricorne hat in particular. After pestering the recruitment office for several days, and down to the last shilling in her purse, she was finally accepted. Ironically, tricorne hats were in short supply and her initial uniform was proudly topped by a Girl Guide beret. Her time in the WRNS seems to have been the best of her life despite some scary times in Plymouth where the bombing was horrendous.

She was sometimes frightened when she came through to where I was sleeping.

'Did you hear all that? They're bombing the army barracks again. Have the doors been blown off?'

'That was last week,' I lied. 'I'll make you a cup of tea and then we'd better get some sleep.'

'I can still smell the fires,' she insisted. 'Yesterday I had to pick my way over the craters in the road to get to work. They were walking the soldiers around, trying to help them get over the shock I suppose. Their faces were horrible, all deadpan and expressionless.'

Doreen had never talked about any of this to me before.

She said she had suffered from what she described as nerves at the time, continually getting up at night and making tea for the rest of the girls; now she often had nightmares.

It was probably fortunate for her health that she was sent to Australia with the Fleet Air Arm. The voyage was not without excitement. One of the officers realised the WRNS did not enjoy such good facilities on board and used to lend them his private bathroom once a week.

'I was sharing the bath with another girl one night when everything was suddenly plunged into darkness,' she said. 'We thought the ship had been torpedoed and could do nothing but pray in the total blackness with our towels and clothes somewhere out of reach.' Fortunately, it was only an electrical fault that was soon rectified.

Doreen was promoted and was proud to be in charge of a group of twenty-four girls. Their work seemed mainly to be concerned with sorting mail but she was a bit vague about that, the social side of life being obviously more interesting. She made many friends. The Australians made the girls welcome, inviting them to their homes for meals and taking them around to see the country. They were also invited to use the facilities of the staff club of the Australian Woman's Weekly magazine.

One night she told me about James, her Australian boyfriend. He was tall with wavy, brown hair and deep, hazel eyes. She said he was polite and well-mannered, unlike the village lads at home. She sighed as she spoke about him.

After the war some of the girls married and stayed on in Australia but my aunt said she had to come home. Her sisters were all married and as the youngest daughter she had to look after her parents. She remembered crying as they lined up on the deck of HMS Victorious to set sail to England from Sydney in 1946. James could be seen in the cheering crowd on the quay below. He waved a big bunch of red roses which he'd been too late to deliver. Hearing about her time in Australia I now understood why she'd kept so many souvenirs. She had wooden boomerangs, koala bears, Aboriginal designed tablecloths and pictures of kangaroos all over the house. The war years had been the best of her life.

After the funeral, my cousin Edith took me aside. 'You must be a saint to have done all you did for Auntie Doreen. I went over every week but couldn't stand more than about half an hour of her at a time.'

My cousin Julia lived in the next village but revealed she'd not been to see her for years. I realised although I lived furthest away, I was probably the person who knew Doreen best. Only I really understood how she had become embittered with her life. For me, she will always be remembered as the perfect maiden aunt.

SOMETHING AND NOTHING

In the space between the corner
and the window
a face.
Long dark hair,
a certain something around her mouth,
tugs
pulls an anchor line tight round my middle.
I can't quite place …
But it's nothing.

An echo lingers,
the way last night's sausages sit on the air.
Something and nothing.
She looks nice though.
A pretty girl.
I'd like her to stay, for a while.
Drink tea,
eat Bourbon Creams.

Her favourites.

Jo Laidlaw

LOVE MATCH

We met coupled
by the birth cord,
grew familiar. We bonded,
enriched by your grace,
oxygenated by our love-ins
and fall

       outs,
by the vigour of your voice.
Familiar to me then,
its rhythmic notes regulate
my heartbeat even now.

Maggie Mackay

An Angel

From a heavenly place
Smiles an angel's face
Sending a message
'I feel so close to you'.
Forever, in my heart
You are the brightest star;
Looking up into the night sky I see
All my sparkling memories.

I will never forget
How much you gave to me.
Even a glimpse is the touch
Of an angel.

Still you dry my tears
And soothe my fears.
It is now forty years.
But this day is still present,
Though the end is not the end,
This we will understand
When we meet our parents
Again.

Christiane Höfel

COME ONE ANGEL

Annie Shirreff

The old man shuffles alongside Frank at the busy road. Even though Frank is barely a teenager, he is a few inches taller than the man. They wait at the cross as the Glasgow City traffic grinds past on green.

'Can you help me across son?'

Frank turns to look in the direction of the voice. He sees an elderly man in a faded tweed coat, his yellowing white hair combed neatly down on both sides. Unlike Frank, he is suitably dressed for the cold weather with a dark wool scarf and matching gloves. Frank looks into the man's eyes. The colour reminds him of faded denim, the shrunken pupils two black dots that quiver at the centre. His back is bent like a crook. It must take some effort for him to raise his head. Frank is reminded of his grandpa.

'Where are you going, Mister?'

The man hesitates, screws his eyes and looks at the two options available in turn. 'Which way are you going?' he asks Frank.

Frank points. 'There.'

'Aye, that's it son. Take my arm will you?'

Although a little taken aback, Frank does as he is bid. He slips one pale, thin hand into the fold of the proffered arm and feels its bone thinness. They wait for the green man.

A passerby might take them for grandpa and grandson. He feels a familiar lurch in his stomach when he thinks of his own grandpa, remembers when he used to visit him and sit at his side watching the football.

'Best team in the world,' Grandpa would say as they watched Celtic.

Frank's interest in football grew from those shared moments on the couch, a packet of crisps and a can of Irn Bru in his hands. Grandpa would sip his beer and occasionally puff on his Old Holborn. Frank can almost smell the tobacco as he remembers the scene. But Grandpa's no longer with them. He died last year. And now Mum's gone too.

When the light changes, Frank and the old man cross from the south side of the Trongate, through the murk of bus exhausts, up into the High Street. The old man walks at a steady pace and Frank, unsure of how to disengage, continues to hold onto his arm.

'Is this far enough, Mister?'

'No, no, a bit further. Just at the top of the hill, son. Not far now.'

'Are you heading for the hospital?' asks Frank.

'Hospital? No son. There's nothing they can do for me there. You're not in a hurry are you?'

'No,' says Frank. He has nowhere to go so why should he be? Might as well walk this old man to where he's going. He'd like to think someone would have done the same for his Grandpa. Maybe there'll be something in it for him.

'Good, good. I could do with some company,' says the old

man. 'What's your name?'

Frank hesitates, seeing as he's not where he's supposed to be. 'Frank,' he answers. 'What's yours?'

The old man pauses for a couple of seconds and stares up and then to the right across the busy street.

'Frank, aye. That's my name too. Funny that.' He continues his slow walk up the hill. 'Francis was my Sunday name. Yours too I'll bet? Only person that ever called me that was my mother.'

'Nobody would ever dare call me Francis.'

'Aye I'm sure,' Francis winks. 'I'll call you Frank then. But you can call me Francis, then nobody'll get us mixed up.'

Frank laughs at the idea.

The two continue in silence until they reach the traffic lights outside Provand's Lordship, the oldest house in Glasgow. Francis points to St Mungo's Museum of Religion on the other side of the road, a modern, honey-coloured stone edifice which resembles a mediaeval building with its towers and turrets. It stands to the front and right of an impressive cathedral. Frank remembers being dragged around all three on some trip with his primary school. He remembers the silence in the Cathedral, the high vaulted roof, the specks of dust that danced in the sunlight which crept through the stained-glass windows. It was one of the few times he'd been inside a church and it almost made him believe there could be a God. But then, wasn't that the point?

'Across there,' says Francis.

'Are you going inside?'

'No. But it's over there.'

They wait for the lights again and cross. Francis looks round and up at the museum. 'It's here somewhere. Let's try round the back. I seem to remember.' He leads Frank by the arm and they reach the bridge to the Glasgow Necropolis.

'Are you meeting someone?' asks Frank.

'Aye, son, that's what it is. I'm meeting someone. She'll not be long. Come with me. She'd like to meet you.'

There's a few tourists walking across the bridge to the graveyard, plenty of folk about, and so Frank follows on as Francis leads.

They walk up the path which curves around the lush, green hillside covered in mausoleums and monuments. Frank is reminded of a visit to his Grandfather in a ward of the Victorian Royal Infirmary which sits at the bottom of the hill next to the Cathedral. The Necropolis could be viewed from the ward window.

'Is that a graveyard, Grandpa?'

'Aye, you'd think building a hospital next to that was in bad taste, eh son?'

'I've never seen stones so big.'

'That's because the once Great and Good of Glasgow are buried there. They thought building themselves bigger stones would show God how important they'd been in this life and that maybe they'd get the same treatment up in Heaven. Well, if there is a God, he'd have taken one look at their hearts and told them it's not money that makes a man good. It's how you treat others in this world.'

The words come back to Frank and he thinks of the way life has treated him this past year, Grandpa dying and then

Mum leaving them.

'I'll come back for you Frank,' she'd said. 'I just need to sort something out for both of us.' But that was six months ago and she never had.

Earlier that morning, Frank had found Dad lying on the couch as usual, the telly still on, the room reeking of smoke and ash, and the empty glass and bottles sticking to the coffee table. He had lifted the debris of last night's binge through to the kitchen, put a duvet over Dad and got ready for school.

Frank had grown four inches over the past few months. His trouser legs and cuffs sat a little high on his ankles and wrists but at least they were clean. Mum had once shown him how to work the machine after complaining about the muck on his football gear. There were a couple of slices of bread left in the cupboard and he made himself some toast, scraping the remnants of jam from the jar and eking it over the surface. At least he'd get a free lunch at school. However, when Frank left the house, he knew he couldn't face going.

He had never really settled in to secondary. Apart from on the football field, he had never got on with the other boys in his year. He started the big school about the same time that Dad lost his job and the fights started. He spent most of that first term in his room at home listening to Mum's complaining and Dad's yelling. And then Mum left and it had stopped. Now the only sounds he hears from his room are Dad staggering around the kitchen or living-room in the small flat. Frank cannot remember the last time Dad slept in the double bed he used to share with Mum.

'Stop a minute son,' says Francis. 'Do you ken who that is? Wee Willie Winkie, running through the toon,' Francis sings. 'That's the man that wrote the song.'

Frank looks at the gravestone and reads the inscription for William Miller. 'Yes, I remember that song. From nursery maybe.' Or was it Dad when he used to put him to bed when he came home from work? Dad was happy then. He never drank. Or only on a Friday.

'Come away now, son. It's up the hill a bit here,' says Francis.

He leads Frank again and they make careful progress up a path which has broken into small pellets of tarmac that make the going a little harder.

'It's a weird place to be meeting someone,' says Frank.

'Meeting someone? Oh aye, that's right. Just up at the top. She always waits there.'

When they reach the top of the hill Francis stops. 'Would you look at that. Those rich folk knew what they were doing when they chose to be buried here. Ha! Their ghouls have got the best view of the city.'

Frank shivers at the thought of all the bones buried beneath the well-tended grass and stones on the hill. He looks down at the impressive view of the city, the Victorian red sandstone tenements sitting alongside the concrete modern ones. A large chimney reaches into the sky, the top hidden by dark grey clouds which hang like a pall of smoke above the scene.

'This is where we court,' says Francis. 'Her family don't like the fact that I'm not one of them.'

'Is that who you're meeting,' says Frank. 'A girlfriend?'

He's quite shocked at the thought.

'Aye, she always meets me here. Look!'

Frank looks in the direction Francis is pointing and sees a woman with red hair and a blue coat making her way up the path towards them. Surely this can't be Francis's girlfriend, she's much too young. As she approaches, Frank's stomach lurches.

'Mum!'

The woman stops just short of the incongruous pair. 'Dad! I thought I'd find you here. Who's this you've got with you?' She looks at a disappointed Frank.

'Frank. I've been keeping him company, said he was meeting someone.' She had looked like his mum – the same hair – but up close he can see this woman is nothing like her.

'Thanks for that, son. I'm Bridget Docherty.' She holds out her hand to Frank. 'He's a wee bit wandered my father. It's his age.'

'Where's my kiss, Moira?' says Francis.

'You mean he's a bit doolally?' asks Frank.

'Aye, I'm a bit doolally about you, Moira,' says Francis. 'That's what I came up here to tell you.'

Bridget smiles at Frank then turns to her father. 'Och, you always were the one. Now, where are we heading today, Francis?'

'Well, I thought we'd just take a wander around here as usual. You don't mind I've brought my wee pal with me, do you?'

'Not at all, a pleasure to meet him. You know, Francis, that cloud looks like rain to me. Why don't we head down to the museum cafe for a nice cup of tea?'

Francis turns his face up to the sky and then smiles widely. 'Café? Aye, that sounds the very thing.'

In the cafe, Bridget asks Frank to mind Francis whilst she orders some tea and muffins. When she returns, she sits at the table holding Francis' hand, occasionally stroking his cheek whilst Frank explains the events of the morning.

'Shouldn't you be at school?' she asks.

'Yes, but I couldnae face it.'

The woman is so kind, it's not long before Frank is telling her about Grandpa, about his mum, and about Dad. Francis sits sipping tea and eating his chocolate muffin. He keeps smiling at Bridget as they talk.

'I told you he's a good boy,' he interjects.

'She said she'd be back for me,' says Frank, 'but she hasnae. She doesnae want me anymore.'

'You know Frank, sometimes people say things, and they mean them at the time. Maybe there's a good reason. Maybe she thought you and your dad would be better off without her.'

'Where's Moira gone?' asks Francis.

'She'll not be long Dad, don't you worry,' Bridget answers.

'Moira was my mother,' she explains to Frank. 'I guess Dad thought he was young again and meeting her as they used to. When they married her family was angry, Francis being Catholic. It's the way it was for some folks, still is, but they came around in the end.'

When they have finished their tea, Bridget eases Francis to his feet and into his coat, wraps his scarf around his neck and helps him on with his gloves.

'Come on Frank, we'll give you a lift home.'

Outside Frank's building, Bridget insists she and Francis accompany him inside to speak to his dad. Dad answers the door and Frank notices he has at least showered and dressed in clean clothes.

'Frank, where have you been? I've had a call from school. They've been worried about you and I was just on the way there.'

'Maybe I should explain,' says Bridget.

Dad invites Bridget and Francis into the house. In the living-room, he grabs the duvet off the couch and settles Francis down on it. Whilst Francis and Frank sit on the couch watching football, Bridget talks to Dad at the table.

'So you helped this old yin and you've been telling them all about us and your mum?' Dad looks angry as he calls across the room to Frank, and then his face crumples.

'Don't you worry, Frank,' says Francis. 'She's a good woman, my Moira.'

Frank hears Dad explain to Bridget about losing his job, about Mum, about everything.

'I know I've lost the plot these last few months, Frank,' Dad calls over again, 'but I'm going to try and change, son. This isnae the first time you've dogged school and I've been far too wound up in myself to notice.'

'Listen, Francis and I better get off. Seems you two have a lot to discuss,' Bridget turns to Frank. 'And thanks again for looking after him.'

'Call me,' says Francis as he reaches into his pocket and hands Frank a scrap of paper. He then reaches around Frank and hugs him.

'Oh, that's the wee note I leave in his pocket in case he gets lost,' says Bridget.

'Like Paddington Bear,' Frank giggles. 'Can I come and visit him?'

'Why of course. Maybe your dad can bring you?' She looks at Dad.

'Aye, aye. No problem,' says Dad.

'And don't worry,' she says to Dad, 'life does get easier. I should know. You owe it to the boy to try and get some help, like I told you.'

Outside the tenement, Bridget opens the car door for Francis whilst Frank and his dad look on. She starts to help him in, but then Francis turns and looks at Frank, winking as he does so.

'Celtic,' he says. 'Best team in the world.'

A BUS RIDE TO HORNSEA

Jackie Burgoyne

Alan looked up the road, eager for the first appearance of the bus. He was distracted for a moment by the sight of a bird's nest in the dusty buddleia growing amongst the bombsite stones. Might there be eggs or fledglings in its grassy bowl? No time to scramble up and find out, even if his dad would let him. The bus was coming round the broad bend and he wanted to feast his eyes on it, to see if it was a model pictured in his cigarette cards. Green and cream, its bull-nosed front reminded him of a picture of a native mask he'd seen in *Adventure Stories for Boys*. This was to be an adventure, to Hornsea by bus. His dad had taken him on bus rides to nearby towns three times now. Each time Alan studied the timetable and learnt the route off by heart. Today's route was Anlaby (Red Lion), Skidby Lane End, Leconfield, Beverley, Brandesburton Hospital, Sigglesthorn, then Hornsea (The Willows).

As they settled into the jolting rhythm of the journey, Alan's dad looked him over, then produced a handkerchief and dabbed at his knee.

'I thought I told you to wash proper.'

Alan knew it was a bruise from one of his bombsite explorations, but didn't say so. You must never answer back.

He gripped his blazer sleeves to keep his frayed cuffs covered, in case they made his dad unhappy too. Why did he have to wear his bloomin' school uniform at the weekend anyway? They passed out of Beverley, away from the narrow terraced houses, past the new council houses, eastwards into farming country.

As the pair climbed down from the bus, seagulls circled overhead, calling to them. Alan's dad smiled down at him and ruffled his hair, then hurriedly straightened it.

'Fill your lungs with that air, son, this is proper seaside, this is.'

Alan watched his dad consult the street signs, then look up and down Russell Avenue for the correct number. He stored every detail of his dad's movements, so he could copy them, when he was back with his friends, exploring the streets of Hessle.

Number 17 had a white wooden gate and a brick path, leading to a semi-detached, pebble-dashed house. To the right of the path was a shrubbery and to the left, a neat rectangular lawn and carefully-pruned rose bushes. Alan held his hand over his eyes, so he could squint at the sun illuminating the yellow and green of the stained glass sunburst above the door.

'Nice looking place, aye son?'

His dad pulled on the brass bell and they were greeted by a short man with a bald head. His remaining hair had been slapped down with Brylcreem, but a few strands had escaped and looked like they were ready to spring into action and cover the gap. He was wearing a grey suit and a thin, striped tie.

'Ow do, Reg.' Alan's dad reached forward and shook the

man's hand.

'Ow do, Leonard. And you must be Alan. Come on in then, come on in.' Reg stood back to allow them to pass into the hall. 'Irene's just coming.'

Irene entered the hallway, wiping her plump hands on a small, lace-edged towel. She was dressed in a smart floral frock and an apron that bore the creases of careful ironing.

'How do you do?' The formality was addressed to Alan's dad. Alan got a look up and down but no greeting. 'Shall we go into the parlour?'

She seemed to be able to speak and purse her lips at the same time. Alan experimented with the expression. Her voice sounded strange. The ordinary Yorkshire voice was familiar to Alan and he had heard posh people talk, his headmaster at school for one. But hers was an odd mix of the two.

The parlour was heavy with tidiness. Brocade curtains hung in the bay window, half-drawn, making the room shadowy despite the sunny day. Antimacassar and lace mats covered every surface. Dark, highly-polished furniture crowded the room. A large cabinet was stuffed with ornaments: a shepherd and shepherdess, dogs, horses and birds, a collection which seemed, to Alan, to have potential for rearranging into some sort of battle. He was considering what might make evenly-matched sides, when Irene interrupted him.

'Did you not take your shoes off at the door? Kindly go and do so. Then go and wash those grubby hands in the cloakroom upstairs.'

There was much here to worry Alan. Was there a sink in this cloakroom? The only one he had seen was in the theatre in

Hull, the year his dad took him to see the pantomime. That was full of coats. Was it alright to reveal his holey socks? Dad was looking uncomfortable too.

'Er, shall I …?' Dad began.

'Oh no. I wouldn't dream of it, just keeping the young man in order,' Irene said.

Dad shot Alan a sympathetic glance.

'Come on lad,' Reg broke in. 'I'll show you what's where.'

When they returned, Alan with clean hands and wearing a pair of Reg's socks, Irene was preparing to serve tea. Alan's tummy rumbled with a hunger fuelled by years of rationing. His eyes lit up at the plates of sandwiches, biscuits and cakes, the like of which he'd never seen outside of a teashop window.

'What a smashing spread Irene,' his dad ventured.

'We're very lucky, what with Reg being in the grocery trade. We never want for anything.'

Alan reached out to the tea trolley. He planned to show his good manners by going for a sandwich before the cakes, but the plate was whipped out from in front of him.

'Not that we would want to encourage the sin of gluttony. Adults first, young man.' Irene squeezed the words from her button-hole mouth.

Alan couldn't understand why, when there was so much food, did everyone seem reluctant to eat it? Irene, especially, was taking tiny bites and resting her sandwich on the plate at regular intervals. He tried to remember, was it 'ask and you don't get' or 'if you don't ask, you don't get'? It seemed safest to stay quiet and avoid Irene's critical eye. He couldn't remember his mother very well, but he was pretty sure she hadn't been like Irene. He knew his dad missed her a lot. Alan had met some of his dad's lady-friends, but he had been told more than once that they wouldn't make much of a mother to him.

The long gaps in conversation were tolled by the ticking of the mantle clock.

Reg broke into the silence. 'How was your school report then, lad?'

'Er, pretty good, Sir,' Alan replied. 'I got a prize from the headmaster for knowing what noise cattle make – it's 'lowing', I heard it in ...' His sentence shrivelled under Irene's severe look.

Reg finally signalled the end of the meal. 'Come on son, I'll show you my bantams.'

Alan noticed his dad's shoulders stiffen, but he nodded his permission. Why did they come to visit these couples he'd never met before, when it always made Dad so miserable? It wasn't much fun for Alan either, they never had any children to play with. And he always felt he was being judged in some way, though he didn't know why.

Alan followed Reg down to the very bottom of the garden, where the afternoon sun shone low over a small wooden henhouse. Six bantams scratched around in a run and ran to the gate when they appeared. Reg showed him how to lay his palm on the back of one of them, so it crouched down, then to cup both hands around its wings, so it could be picked up without flapping. The bird settled in his arms and clucked gently, looking sideways at him with one beady orange eye.

'If you stop with us, you can help me with them. Clip their wings and that.'

Stop? Alan hadn't heard any talk of stopping over. It was like that other lady, in Whitby, who had shown him the bedroom with cowboy wallpaper. He didn't stop over that time. Anyway, he didn't have any pyjamas with him. He didn't have any pyjamas at all. He put the worry from his mind, as Reg took him round to the nest box at the back of the henhouse and let him lift the heavy lid to reveal a clutch of four tiny eggs.

'Go on lad, pick them up. You can take one home for your breakfast if you like. Serve it in a thimble, aye?'

Alan gently lifted the eggs from their nest. Passing them one by one to Reg, he cradled the fourth in his hand. He followed the path back to the house, staring at the egg, practicing the degree of gentleness required to keep it safe without crushing it. Reg walked next to him, his arm half round his shoulder. Alan looked up and saw his dad had come to the door. He had a deep frown on his face.

'Come on Alan, we're off.'

Alan couldn't decide whether to be more shocked by his dad's abrupt ending of the afternoon or that he was holding three sandwiches and taking big bites out of them as he spoke. They passed Irene in the hallway, where she stood flapping a tea towel in front of her face and saying 'oh my, oh my.' Alan turned back for a moment to look at Reg, who shrugged his shoulders and gave a wry smile.

Later that night, as Alan curled up in a corner of his dad's lodging house bed, he wondered what the visit had been all about. In the box in which he kept his belongings was the bantam egg, which had survived the long bus journey home.

FLYING THE NEST

Sandy Hashimi

'Give it a fortnight and you will know everything there is to know!' Mrs Hunter had promised as she launched her daughter into the steaming train two weeks earlier. But Abigail Hunter was still feeling like a calf in a cuckoo's nest, wondering if she would ever fit in to what her employer considered to be the hub of the intelligentsia but which was to everyone else a small second-hand bookshop just off The Strand.

The proprietress, Mathilda Croft-Sperry, had no such misgivings about the eighteen-year-old farmer's daughter. She believed her apprentice, once her heritage was encouraged to blossom, would add a soupçon of the unorthodox to her little establishment. Employing the young Miss Hunter, whilst the child was both naïve and maladroit, was for Miss Croft-Sperry an ace-in-the-making to be proffered with a flourish at those who thought her a stuffy stick-in-the-mud.

By the dawn of the 1930s a growing number of women were seeking new opportunities for employment and Miss Croft-Sperry had received a dozen applications in response to her humble advertisement. An applicant's tidiness was judged by a lack of ink blots and smudges on the letter of application and their literacy by the meticulous crossing of t's and dotting of i's. She supposed the frantic urgency of wartime correspondence might have despatched some of the niceties of calligraphy during that uncertain period, but she would not excuse the growing habit of allowing the cross of a t to float, four characters removed from its vertical stalk, nor the looping of an l, which created a niggling hole in a word where none belonged. However, Mathilda Croft-Sperry, whilst she brooked no compromise in literacy, earnestly sought some distinctive quality that might elevate and enliven her own childless existence and offer a fertile pasture into which to drill her collected seeds of wisdom.

Those applicants who succeeded in the first part of the process were then subjected to what she liked to call her Sherlock Holmes System. Such labours could reveal hidden gems the written application did not, and in the parochial Miss Abigail Hunter's case, Miss Croft-Sperry believed she might indeed have mined her very own diamond in the rough. For through the time-consuming study of indexes and publishing sheets she had discovered this young lady was the daughter of an author. Well worth, indeed, the consumption of several cups of honeyed tea and her entire stock of emergency crème patisseries with sugared greengages that such laborious searching had necessitated.

It should be explained here that the book was little more than a pamphlet, the subject of which was the breeding of Hereford cattle. But it was the language used that ignited Miss Croft-Sperry's insulin-starved blood. Mr Hunter's unassuming tome had gained some modest celebrity in County circles for his earthy descriptions of animal husbandry. He pronounced the Hereford's masculine appendage as a *penicle stalactite* and, as a professed expert on *mountificated progeneration*, warned of the perils of *spermical alienation*. Miss Croft-Sperry, wishing her clientele to realise she had not only read such language but positively basked in its mordacious murkiness, had grasped such gritty grammar with both of her fat white hands.

She imagined introducing the modest girl as 'Mr Brian Hunter's daughter ... oh, you know, the famous author of *Animal Attraction: When Size Matters.'* No less important was the ancestral influence such a glossologist might impart on his offspring and after all Miss Croft-Sperry had been following the most fascinating concept of eugenics, currently gaining critical acclaim in the newspapers. At last the proprietress saw victory at the Scrabble games between her establishment and that of Miss Elliot's haberdashery, over which her acute sense of competitiveness, and the petite fours consumed in preparation for battle, caused such vexing indigestion on a monthly basis.

Abigail herself was unaware of these machinations. When she had applied for a number of positions in the capital she had entertained little hope of gaining any consequential employment. Instead, she accepted that as a rosy-cheeked, somewhat stocky and shy young woman the best she might hope for was a place in a grand house – perhaps as a mother's help or a kitchen assistant. It had been her own mother's suggestion that she cast her net a little wider and apply for the position of bookshop assistant advertised in the smallest of print in The Times. Not that the farm usually received this newspaper. Its wilting pages had wrapped the delivery from

Fuller's fishmonger, and upon reading it Mrs Hunter declared the fact the Situations Vacant had accompanied the smoked haddock, if not quite a miracle of the loaves and fishes variety, was indeed a visitation from fate herself.

It was during a particularly stuffy August afternoon, when the dust motes hung like tiny crystals in the stripes of sunlight piercing the dusky interior and while Abigail was rubbing out the pencilled marks on the velum of a recent acquisition, that Monsieur L'Éclair set the little brass bell above the door a-ding-a-linging, trailing a welcome breeze in the wake of his tailored pin-striped suit. Noticing the new arrival, Abigail's employer set her chins merrily jiggling as she nodded towards the high-back chair resting against the science section.

'Do take a seat, I shall be with you presently,' she chirruped and hurried her persuasion of Mrs Freemason that nowhere else in the metropolis could you purchase a bound set of Dickens' works for one pound, ten shillings and sixpence.

Mr L'Éclair showed no signs of taking the weight off his calf-skin loafers and instead stood in front of the small oak table at which Abigail toiled with her eraser, blowing little puffs of warm breath at the wisps of pencil-stained rubber that lay like breadcrumbs across the page. When she raised her eyes she noticed the gentleman looking over her shoulder at the stuffed barn owl standing guard from the top of the travellers' tales bookcase behind her.

'He is quite magnificent, isn't he?' His voice was like whipped cream. The words ran smoothly into each other and swirled around Abigail's ears licking at her pink cheeks.

'Yes, I suppose so,' she whispered and stood to attention.

And because the customer remained, his head cocked and his hazelnut eyes fixed on the bird of prey, Abigail felt compelled to continue.

'It's a barn owl. They're quite common in the countryside.'

'Yes, in France too. How long have you had such a fine creature watching over you and your books?'

Swimming in the liquid vowels and consonants, Abigail had quite forgotten to be nervous and rewarded the customer with a wide smile.

'My employer says he is as old as Christ's crucifixion!' she whispered conspiratorially and her even white teeth shone against skin considered altogether too brown for the city but quite acceptable a hundred or so miles away where the sun stained everyone a standard antique pine.

'Ah! I think that might be a slight exaggeration, don't you?' The Frenchman returned her smile with a wink. 'Tell me, are you interested in birds?'

Abigail was now gliding over familiar ground and the tone of longing strengthened her voice.

'Oh yes, I miss them so. On the farm we set our seasons by the first cuckoo, the swallows returning from the south and the song thrush building her nest. Here there appear to be only pigeons and the occasional ...'

'Carry on, Miss Hunter.'

Miss Croft-Sperry had stoutly swooped upon the Frenchman and set about guiding him towards her own counter. Abigail realised then how much her employer resembled a bird herself, albeit a rather plump turkey, with her slightly hooked nose, small shiny eyes and the layers of pink gizzard resting on her tight lace collar.

'Monsieur L'Éclair, how delightful to see you again.'

'Thank you, Mademoiselle. I was being thoroughly educated by your young assistant and …'

'Quite so. Now, what may I do for you today? Verse? Or perhaps something by one of your French compatriots, to make you feel at home …?'

Later, as Abigail prepared for bed she pondered on her employer's age. To her untrained eye she had seemed ancient, but from the animated arm-flapping and eyelash fluttering Monsieur L'Éclair's visit had fomented she now speculated that Miss Croft-Sperry might be her own mother's age and therefore somewhere in her early forties. Monsieur L'Éclair, probably in his early thirties if Abigail was any judge, seemed oblivious to the florid cheeks and girlish clucking, glancing good-naturedly over his shoulder at the young apprentice whenever her employer's back was turned in the act of producing yet another must-have book.

Eventually his purchase had been brought to Abigail's table to be parcelled and stringed: a rather dull epistle on 19th century church fonts. Abigail had felt a little dismayed. As she lay in her bed listening to her employer's heavy footfall on the creaking stair intent on liberating another crème patisserie – the only thing that aided her insomnia, poor woman – Abigail imagined the words waiting expectantly below her in the shop. In her mind all those forgotten vowels and consonants clamoured against their covers for release, words which had flowed from the fountain pens of a thousand authors, petrified into print, and imprisoned in their leather tombs. Some would never be released, while others – the lucky ones – would be reborn and fly through the eyes of the reader to breed and duplicate in an arable mind. With all that was on offer in the shop, church fonts did not seem to deserve such preferential treatment.

At the same time as her assistant was imagining a churning sea of chained text, Mathilda Croft-Sperry, licking a finger and collecting the last morsel of flaky pastry from the yellow china plate, was thinking about how to let her apprentice go with the minimum of fuss. It was a fact that Miss Hunter had followed her employer's instructions to the letter, there was no complaint to be realised there. She had even taken on additional tasks the proprietress found unpalatable, such as setting the wickedly sharp jaws of the mousetraps and emptying them on a weekly basis, despatching the limp victims with undaunted resolve. However, she had proved a very great disappointment as far as the Scrabble was concerned. Her addition at the table had been no help at all, despite her employer's gentle urgings to *think like your father* and *remember animal husbandry*. All such encouragement had met with a stunned silence and Miss Hunter's greatest achievement to date had been the word *crankle*, which hadn't even managed a double letter score. As for her vivacious heritage, Miss Croft-Sperry was beginning to realise it was nigh on impossible to introduce the phrase *penicle stalactite* into everyday conversations without someone asking if she needed a glass of water or offering a chair on which to sit her plenteous posterior.

The weeks passed while the employer periodically considered the best way to justify dismissing her employee to customers who had grown accustomed to her presence. In the meantime the dour young woman seemed to blossom into the very epitome of a good and faithful servant. She had taken to carrying out tasks before her employer realised they required doing and the pantry was never short of a sweet pastry or tartlet at times of urgent need, of which there were plenty. Miss Croft-Sperry assumed Miss Hunter's burgeoning aura of sophistication in style of dress and comportment was a mixture of the city's metropolitan influence and her own fine example. Monsieur L'Éclair continued to visit the shop periodically but seemed not to notice Miss Hunter at all. Nevertheless, Mathilda Croft-Sperry was no fool, and she continued to send her apprentice off on errands to the confectioners whenever she felt the familiar hummingbird flutter against her well-covered ribs, which inevitably accompanied the first sight of the Frenchman on the pavement outside.

Her relief that she had dithered at dispensing the girl back to Devizes was compounded as pride flooded her narrowed arteries when her protégé (for that is how she was beginning to view the young woman) spelled out the word *zygote* in a particularly triumphant Scrabble battle, bagging a triple word score in excess of a century.

Life at the second-hand bookshop might have continued in smooth sociability but for two things: all good employers now gave their staff at least one week's paid annual holiday, and Abigail Hunter had blossomed from the inside out.

'My dear, are you sure you need such a large bag?' Miss Croft-Sperry asked kindly as her charge struggled across the boards of the shop half-dragging a suitcase of such proportions that it bounced clumsily on her trim silk-stockinged ankles.

'Well, you see, I ...' started Abigail who had more than her usual high colour in her cheeks.

'No, no ... I do see perfectly. You no doubt wish to show off your new elegance to your dear parents. How proud they will be! I understand completely.' For her apprentice had become quite the fashionable Miss, making her own neat dresses and indeed, the occasional skirt for her employer from material she found in the various markets she frequented on her days off.

'I just wanted to say ...' but Abigail's words were cut short by the tinkling of the little brass bell and both women's heads turned towards the open door in which was framed Monsieur L'Éclair in all his continental glory.

'Off you go then,' ushered Miss Croft-Sperry, now anxious to be alone and able to divert all her attentions to the object of her overweight affections.

Abigail merely nodded, relieved that matters now appeared clear and allowed Pierre L'Éclair to take the weighty case from her sore hands and deposit it into the boot of his waiting Ford Model T. Opening the passenger door he helped her into the nest of smooth leather and polished chrome with gentlemanly concern, tucking the hem of her dress out of harm's way. As he walked around the back of the vehicle to his own door his eyes caught those of the shop's proprietress and he gave a cheery wave, leaving Mathilda Croft-Sperry leaning against the sparse romance section, her mouth a perfect 'o', through which small clucking noises escaped unbidden under the watchful eye of a wise old barn owl.

CANNAS AND CORDYLINES

Cannas and cordylines guided me
through the gates;
sunbursts, rude red-copper,
in rows along the fence.

These days palm fronds thud like sentries
fainting after days on duty,
as my head, bearing a dry season too,
mulches half dreams,
faded senses.

Maggie Mackay

COMPLEXION

She wears laughter's brushstrokes
on nut-brown skin.
It's an elastic witness
to life's follies,
ninety summers on.
Powdered by rose-blush pats of rouge
and kisses of gloss-grape lipstick,
that face has prospered
past sleepless nights,
two coronations, frozen pipes,
the grimy filth of an infernal world war.

Maggie Mackay

The Jam's Not In The Dish

You twitter
in your clotted tongue,
tremors pluck
at pocket lips,
fluffy head, rinsed in blue,
nods an apology
for scattered juice.

I witter on,
trying to discover
what you wish to say
but it's already lost
in history
just
> *The jam's not in the dish*

or as rheumy orbs
seek aeons past
> *Where's your Dad?*

It's a bitter lesson
you teach,
stern spine bowed,
gnarled by nipping digits,
mind mashed,
sweet wisdom seeping through,

but never be sorry,
you tended your seeds,
    harvested
        fresh fruit.

I am the keeper of your story
so
mutter, twitter, moan,
Who made that awful mess?
or as I pass the marmalade,
    What bugger stole the jam?

Maureen Cullen

The Writers

Elizabeth Angus

is completing an Open University honours degree in Literature. Inspired by her former English teacher (now a respected author), she is finally working to make her lifelong dream of writing success a reality. Her first taste of fame came at the age of eleven, with a poem in the local paper, and she has also been published in an anthology of flash fiction. Raised on the Hebridean island of Islay, she now shares a cottage beside Loch Lomond with her husband, their elderly cat, and far too many books. She has a passion for the natural world, a burning curiosity about almost everything, and finds peace of mind by climbing mountains.

Hilary Berry

has recently retired and is relishing the opportunity to indulge herself, resurrecting old hobbies and discovering new interests such as creative writing. She has already had three short stories published in local anthologies.

Viki Birchall

has been a housewife since the birth of her third child five years ago put an end to her career as a Performance Manager. Now she fills her days cooking, cleaning and carrying out countless other chores. A chatty fly-on-the-wall might, however, tell you that she spends an awful lot of time reading, writing and taking long walks down her native North East coastline. During the school holidays Viki likes to travel with her family around Britain and Europe in their big, green van.

JACKIE BURGOYNE

writes from her home on a wild and stormy part of the Dorset coast. She draws on an eclectic employment history, including working as a waitress, a sweet shop assistant, a midwife, a social science researcher and a children's reading partner. She is happiest when walking along the local beaches and cliffs, thinking about character, setting and plot.

MAUREEN CULLEN

lives in Peterborough and is a Scot with strong ties to her home in the West of Scotland. She is pursuing her love of writing through creative writing courses at the Open University. She is a keen tennis and athletics fan and swims daily. She loves cooking and wine. She keeps a close eye on political and social issues. Her favourite poet is Louis MacNeice. She is pleased to have had poems published in Writers' Forum, Reach Poetry, and Poetry Scotland's 'Open Mouse' website.

SANDY HASHIMI

lives on the south coast of Dorset and works in a local primary school. She enjoys writing poetry, short stories and novels, often inspired by her love of history and genealogy. She has written a tour guide for her local town and recently three of her short stories appeared in a paperback anthology. Sandy has just completed a History (Hons) Degree with the Open University and now hopes to be able to devote more time to her creative writing. Among her favourite authors are Hilary Mantel, Sylvia Townsend Warner, Bernard Cornwell and Neil Gaiman.

CHRISTIANE HÖFEL,

songwriter, has liked reading and writing since she was a child. What was a teddy bear for other children was, for her, a book. Difficult childhood experiences inspired her to put her thoughts on paper, aiming to help readers overcome a crisis after losing a beloved person. She has also founded an international network for social projects involved with chess. She has published an article about the World Chess Projects Network and a poem in a local newspaper. Her favourite authors are Simon Beckett, Kathy Reichs, J.K. Rowling and Stephen King.

JO LAIDLAW

is a freelance copywriter, writing for some of the world's best-known companies. She is working on a collection of poetry and has reached the beginning of the middle of her first novel. She's recently been published in Writers' Forum and was placed in the Hysteria 2012 Anthology. Jo lives near Edinburgh with her husband and son, where she also reviews restaurants and makes excuses not to go cycling.

LYNN LOVE

After writing fiction in her youth, Lynn returned to it with vigour in 2008, having completed her honours degree with the Open University and finding it impossible to tear herself away from the keyboard. Her lifelong love of fiction and history were fused when Lynn was given an Elizabethan sixpence, inspiring her to write a Young Adult fantasy novel where the coin is the key to adventures through time. Lynn has drafted two other novels and is currently working with a literary consultant with the aim of becoming a published author in her own right.

SHARON MACGREGOR

lives in Glasgow with her partner and four children. After eighteen years of child rearing and teaching English to young people with special needs, she decided to squeeze some time for herself and take a course in creative writing with the Open University. She loves to write both short stories and poetry and is delighted to have had publishing success in two anthologies: *Sea of Ink* and *New Writing Scotland 31*.

MAGGIE MACKAY,

a retired learning support teacher, has discovered her inner poet through the Open University experience and is delighted to be published three times by Writers' Forum, Poetry Scotland and in Ink Pantry Publishing's *Sea of Ink*. A Scot, she loves to travel both across the globe and in her head, just as much as she enjoys good food and wine. One day she will get round to learning how to put up bookshelves. For now, she likes taking books off the shelves, and reading them. Her favourite poets are Tony Harrison, Marie Howe, Norman

McCaig and Shakespeare, not necessarily in that order.

ANNIE SHIRREFF

lives in Scotland, where she spends much of her time looking out of the kitchen window wondering what her characters will do next. These are her first published short stories since completing a writing course with The Open University.

PAUL STEPHENSON

lives in North East England and is currently pursuing a career writing fiction. He has an avid interest in writing creatively, along with other artistic and creative pursuits: creating tattoo designs, illustrations, designing and painting decorative indoor murals. He is currently working on (among other projects) the third draft of his first novel, as well as studying towards an Open Degree (with honours) with the Open University.